The
of the Novels and Selected Writings
of Daniel Defoe

ROBINSON CRUSOE

Volume II

The Life & Strange Surprizing ADVENTURES of ROBINSON CRUSOE

Of *YORK*, MARINER

Who lived Eight and Twenty Years, all alone in an un-inhabited Island on the Coast of AMERICA, near the Mouth of the Great River of Oroonoque;

Having been cast on Shore by Shipwreck, wherein all the Men perished but himself.

WITH an Account how he was at last as strangely deliver'd by PYRATES.

Written by Himself

Volume II

OXFORD: BASIL BLACKWELL
Publisher to the SHAKESPEARE HEAD PRESS
of STRATFORD-UPON-AVON
1927

FIRST PUBLISHED BY THE
SHAKESPEARE HEAD PRESS IN 1927
REPRINTED IN GREAT BRITAIN BY
PHOTO OFFSET 1974 BY
WILLIAM CLOWES & SONS, LIMITED,
LONDON, BECCLES AND COLCHESTER

ISBN 0 900659 19 X

CONTENTS

THE ILLUSTRATIONS

For a Note on the Illustrations see Volume I, page vii.

THE LIFE AND ADVENTURES OF ROBINSON CRUSOE,

&c.

DURING the long Time that *Friday* has now been with me, and that he began to speak to me, and understand me, I was not wanting to lay a Foundation of Religious Knowledge in his Mind; particularly I ask'd him one Time who made him? The poor Creature did not understand me at all, but thought I had ask'd him who was his Father; but I took it by another handle, and ask'd him who made the Sea, the Ground we walk'd on, and the Hills, and Woods; he told me it was one old *Benamuckee*, that liv'd beyond all: He could describe nothing of this great Person, but that he was very old; much older he said than the Sea, or the Land; than the Moon, or the Stars: I ask'd him then, if this old Person had made all Things, why did not all Things worship him; he look'd very grave and with a perfect Look of Innocence, said, *All Things do say O to him:* I ask'd him if the People who die in his Country went away any where; he said, yes, they all went to *Benamuckee:* then I ask'd him whether these they eat up went thither too? He said yes.

From these Things, I began to instruct him in the Knowledge of the true God: I told him that the great Maker of all Things liv'd up there, pointing up towards Heaven: That he governs the World by the same Power and Providence by which he had made it: That he was omnipotent, could do every Thing for us, give every Thing to us, take every Thing from us; and thus by Degrees I open'd his Eyes. He listned with great Attention, and receiv'd with Pleasure the Notion of *Jesus Christ* being sent to redeem us, and of the Manner of making our Prayers to God, and his being able to hear us, even into Heaven; he told me one Day, that if our God could hear us up beyond the Sun, he must needs be a greater God than their *Benamuckee*, who liv'd but a little way off, and yet could not hear, till they went up to the great Mountains where he dwelt, to speak to him; I ask'd him if ever he went thither, to speak to him; he said no, they never went that were young Men; none went thither but the old Men, who he call'd their *Oowocakee*, that is, as I made him explain it to me, their Religious, or Clergy, and that they went to say *O*, (so he call'd saying Prayers) and then came back, and told them what *Benamuckee* said: By this I observ'd, That there is *Priestcraft*, even amongst the most blinded ignorant Pagans in the World; and the Policy of making a secret Religion, in order to preserve the Veneration of the People to the Clergy, is not only to be found in the *Roman*, but perhaps among all Religions in the World, even among the most brutish and barbarous Savages.

I endeavour'd to clear up this Fraud, to my Man *Friday*, and told him, that the Pretence of their old Men going up the Mountains, to say *O* to their God *Benamuckee*, was a Cheat, and their bringing Word from thence what he said, was much more so; that if they met with any Answer, or spake with any one there, it must be with an evil Spirit: And then I entred into a long Discourse with him about the Devil, the Original of him, his Rebellion against God, his Enmity to Man, the Reason of it, his setting himself up in the dark Parts of the World to be Worship'd instead of God, and as God; and the many Stratagems he made use of to delude Mankind to his Ruine; how he had a secret access to our Passions, and to our affections, to adapt his Snares so to our Inclinations, as to cause us even to be our own Tempters, and to run upon our Destruction by our own Choice.

I found it was not so easie to imprint right Notions in his Mind about the Devil, as it was about the Being of a God. Nature assisted all my Arguments to Evidence to him, even the Necessity of a great first Cause and overruling governing Power; a secret directing Providence, and of the Equity, and Justice, of paying Homage to him that made us, and the like. But there appeared nothing of all this in the Notion of an evil Spirit; of his Original, his Being, his Nature, and above all of his Inclination to do Evil, and to draw us in to do so too; and the poor Creature puzzl'd me once in such a manner, by a Question meerly natural and innocent, that I scarce knew what to say to him. I had been talking a great deal to him of the Power of God, his Omnipotence, his dreadful Nature to Sin, his being a consuming Fire to the Workers of Iniquity; how, as he had made us all, he could destroy us and all the World in a Moment; and he listen'd with great Seriousness to me all the while.

After this, I had been telling him how the Devil was God's Enemy in the Hearts of Men, and used all his Malice and Skill to defeat the good Designs of Providence, and to ruine the Kingdom of Christ in the World; and the like. Well, says *Friday*, but you say, God is so strong, so great, is he not much strong, much might as the Devil? Yes, yes, says I, *Friday*, God is stronger than the Devil, God is above the Devil, and therefore we pray to God to tread him down under our Feet, and enable us to resist his Temptations and quench his fiery Darts. *But*, says he again, *if God much strong, much might as the Devil, why God no kill the Devil, so make him no more do wicked?*

I was strangely surpriz'd at his Question, and after all, tho' I was now an old Man, yet I was but a young Doctor, and ill enough quallified for a Casuist, or a Solver of Difficulties: And at first I could not tell what to say, so I pretended not to hear him, and ask'd him what he said? But he was too earnest for an Answer to forget his Question; so that he repeated it in the very same broken Words, as above. By this time I had recovered my self a little, and I said, *God will at last punish him severely*; he is *reserv'd for the Judgment, and is to be cast into the Bottomless-Pit, to dwell with everlasting Fire*: This did not satisfie *Friday*, but he returns upon me, repeating my Words, RESERVE, AT LAST, *me no understand*; *but*, *Why not kill the Devil now, not kill great ago?* You may as well ask me, *said I*, Why God does not kill you and I, when we do wicked Things here that offend him? We are preserv'd to repent and be pardon'd; He muses a while at this; *well*, *well*, says he, mighty affectionately, *that well; so you, I, Devil, all wicked, all preserve, repent, God pardon all.* Here I was run down again by him to the last Degree, and it was a Testimony to me, how the meer Notions of Nature, though they will guide reasonable Creatures to the Knowledge of a God, and of a Worship or Homage due to the supreme Being, of God as the Consequence of our Nature; yet nothing but divine Revelation can from the Knowledge of *Jesus Christ*, and of a Redemption purchas'd for us, of a Mediator of the new Covenant, and of an Intercessor, at the Foot-stool of God's Throne; I say, nothing but a Revelation from Heaven, can form these in the Soul, and that therefore the Gospel of our Lord and Saviour *Jesus Christ*; I mean, the Word of God, and the Spirit of God promis'd for the Guide and Sanctifier of his People, are the absolutely necessary Instructors of the Souls of Men, in the saving Knowledge of God, and the Means of Salvation.

I therefore diverted the present Discourse between me and my Man, rising up hastily, as upon some sudden Occasion of going out; then sending him for something a good way off, I seriously pray'd to God that he would enable me to instruct savingly this poor Savage, assisting by his Spirit the Heart of the poor ignorant Creature, to receive the Light of the Knowledge of God in *Christ*, reconciling him to himself, and would guide me to speak so to him from the Word of God, as his Conscience might be convinc'd, his Eyes open'd, and his Soul sav'd. When he came again to me, I entred into a long Discourse with him upon the Subject of the Redemption of Man by the Saviour of the World, and of the Doctrine of the Gospel preach'd from Heaven, *viz.* of Repentance towards God, and Faith in our Blessed Lord *Jesus*. I then explain'd to him, as well as I could, why our Blessed Redeemer took not on him the Nature of Angels, but the Seed of *Abraham*, and how for that Reason the fallen Angels had no Share in the Redemption; that he came only to the lost Sheep of the House of *Israel*, and the like.

I had, *God knows*, more Sincerity than Knowledge, in all the Methods I took for this poor Creature's Instruction, and must acknowledge what I believe all that act upon the same Principle will find, That in laying Things open to him, I really inform'd and instructed myself in many Things, that either I did not know, or had not fully consider'd before; but which occurr'd naturally to my

Mind, upon my searching into them, for the Information of this poor Savage: and I had more Affection in my Enquiry after Things upon this Occasion, than ever I felt before; so that whether this poor wild Wretch was the better for me, or no, I had great Reason to be thankful that ever he came to me: My Grief set lighter upon me, my Habitation grew comfortable to me beyond Measure; and when I reflected that in this solitary Life which I had been confin'd to, I had not only been moved my self to look up to Heaven, and to seek to the Hand that had brought me there; but was now to be made an Instrument under Providence to save the Life, and *for ought I knew*, the Soul of a poor Savage, and bring him to the true Knowledge of Religion, and of the Christian Doctrine, that he might know Christ Jesus, *to know whom is Life eternal.* I say, when I reflected upon all these Things, a secret Joy run through every Part of my Soul, and I frequently rejoyc'd that ever I was brought to this Place, which I had so often thought the most dreadful of all Afflictions that could possibly have befallen me.

In this thankful Frame I continu'd all the Remainder of my Time, and the Conversation which employ'd the Hours between *Friday* and I, was such, as made the three Years which we liv'd there together perfectly and compleatly happy, *if any such Thing as compleat Happiness can be form'd in a sublunary State.* The Savage was now a good Christian, a much better than I; though I have reason to hope, and bless God for it, that we were equally penitent, and comforted restor'd Penitents; we had here the Word of God to read, and no farther off from his Spirit to instruct, than if we had been in *England.*

I always apply'd my self in Reading the Scripture, to let him know, as well as I could, the Meaning of what I read; and he again, by his serious Enquiries, and Questionings, made me, *as I said before*, a much better Scholar in the Scripture Knowledge, than I should ever have been by my own private meer Reading. Another thing I cannot refrain from observing here also from Experience, in this retir'd Part of my Life, *viz.* How infinite, and inexpressible a Blessing it is, that the Knowledge of God, and of the Doctrine of Salvation by *Christ Jesus*, is so plainly laid down in the Word of God; so easy to be receiv'd and understood: That as the bare reading the Scripture made me capable of understanding enough of my Duty, to carry me directly on to the great Work of sincere Repentance for my Sins, and laying hold of a Saviour for Life and Salvation, to a stated Reformation in Practice, and Obedience to all God's Commands, and this without any Teacher or Instructer; I mean, humane; so the same plain Instruction sufficiently serv'd to the enlightning this Savage Creature, and bringing him to be such a Christian, as I have known few equal to him in my Life.

As to all the Disputes, Wranglings, Strife and Contention, which has happen'd in the World about Religion, whether Niceties in Doctrines, or Schemes of Church Government, they were all perfectly useless to us; as for ought I can yet see, they have been to all the rest of the World: We had the *sure Guide* to Heaven, *viz.* The Word of God; and we had, *blessed be God*, comfortable Views of the Spirit of God teaching and instructing us by his Word, *leading us into all Truth*, and making us both willing and obedient to the Instruction of his Word, and I cannot see the least Use that the greatest Knowledge of the disputed Points in Religion which have made such Confusions in the World would have been to us, if we could have obtain'd it; but I must go on with the

Historical Part of Things, and take every Part in its order.

After *Friday* and I became more intimately acquainted, and that he could understand almost all I said to him, and speak fluently, though in broken *English* to me; I acquainted him with my own Story, or at least so much of it as related to my coming into the Place, how I had liv'd there, and how long. I let him into the Mystery, for such it was to him, of Gunpowder, and Bullet, and taught him how to shoot: I gave him a Knife, which he was wonderfully delighted with, and I made him a Belt, with a Frog hanging to it, such as in *England* we wear Hangers in; and in the Frog, instead of a Hanger, I gave him a Hatchet, which was not only as good a Weapon in some Cases, but much more useful upon other Occasions.

I describ'd to him the Country of *Europe*, and particularly *England*, which I came from; how we liv'd, how we worshipp'd God, how we behav'd to one another; and how we traded in Ships to all Parts of the World: I gave him an Account of the Wreck which I had been on board of, and shew'd him as near as I could, the Place where she lay; but she was all beaten in Pieces before, and gone.

I shew'd him the Ruins of our Boat, which we lost when we escap'd, and which I could not stir with my whole Strength then; but was now fallen almost to Pieces: Upon seeing this Boat, *Friday* stood musing a great while, and said nothing; I ask'd him what it was he study'd upon, at last says he, *me see such Boat like come to Place at my Nation.*

I did not understand him a good while; but at last, when I had examin'd farther into it, I understood by him, that a Boat, such as that had been, came on Shore upon the Country where he liv'd; that is, as he explain'd it, was driven thither by Stress of Weather: I presently imagin'd, that some *European* Ship muſt have been caſt away upon their Coaſt, and the Boat might get loose, and drive a Shore; but was so dull, that I never once thought of Men making escape from a Wreck thither, much less whence they might come; so I only enquir'd after a Description of the Boat.

Friday describ'd the Boat to me well enough; but brought me better to underſtand him, when he added with some Warmth, *we save the White Mans from drown:* Then I presently ask'd him, if there was any *white Mans*, as he call'd them, in the Boat; *yes*, he said, *the Boat full white Mans:* I ask'd him how many; he told upon his Fingers seventeen: I ask'd him then what become of them; he told me, *they live*, *they dwell at my Nation.*

This put new Thoughts into my Head; for I presently imagin'd, that these might be the Men belonging to the Ship, that was caſt away in Sight of *my Island*, as I now call it; and who after the Ship was ſtruck on the Rock, and they saw her inevitably loſt, had sav'd themselves in their Boat, and were landed upon that wild Shore among the Savages.

Upon this, I enquir'd of him more critically, What was become of them? He assur'd me they lived ſtill there; that they had been there about four Years; that the Savages let them alone, and gave them Victuals to live. I ask'd him, How it came to pass they did not kill them and eat them? He said, *No, they make Brother with them;* that is, as I underſtood him, a Truce: And then he added, *They no eat Mans but when makes the War fight*; that is to say, they never eat any Men but such as come to fight with them, and are taken in Battle.

It was after this some considerable Time, that being

upon the Top of the Hill, at the *East* Side of the Island, from whence as I have said, I had in a clear Day discover'd the Main, or Continent of *America*; *Friday*, the Weather being very serene, looks very earnestly towards the Main Land, and in a kind of Surprise, falls a jumping and dancing, and calls out to me, for I was at some Distance from him: I ask'd him, What was the Matter? *O joy!* Says he, *O glad! There see my Country, there my Nation!*

I observ'd an extraordinary Sense of Pleasure appear'd in his Face, and his Eyes sparkled, and his Countenance discover'd a strange Eagerness, as if he had a Mind to be in his own Country again; and this Observation of mine, put a great many Thoughts into me, which made me at first not so easy about my new Man *Friday* as I was before; and I made no doubt, but that if *Friday* could get back to his own Nation again, he would not only forget all his Religion, but all his Obligation to me; and would be forward enough to give his Countrymen an Account of me, and come back perhaps with a hundred or two of them, and make a Feast upon me, at which he might be as merry as he us'd to be with those of his Enemies, when they were taken in War.

But I wrong'd the poor honest Creature very much, for which I was very sorry afterwards. However as my Jealousy encreased, and held me some Weeks, I was a little more circumspect, and not so familiar and kind to him as before; in which I was certainly in the Wrong too, the honest grateful Creature having no thought about it, but what consisted with the best Principles, both as a religious Christian, and as a grateful Friend, as appeared afterwards to my full Satisfaction.

While my Jealousy of him lasted, you may be sure I

was every Day pumping him to see if he would discover any of the new Thoughts, which I suspected were in him; but I found every thing he said was so Honest, and so Innocent, that I could find nothing to nourish my Suspicion; and in spight of all my Uneasiness he made me at last entirely his own again, nor did he in the least perceive that I was Uneasie, and therefore I could not suspect him of Deceit.

One Day walking up the same Hill, but the Weather being haizy at Sea, so that we could not see the Continent, I call'd to him, and said, *Friday*, do not you wish your self in your own Country, your own Nation? Yes, he said, *he be much O glad to be at his own Nation*. What would you do there said I, would you turn Wild again, eat Mens Flesh again, and be a Savage as you were before. He lookt full of Concern, and shaking his Head said, *No no*, Friday *tell them to live Good*, tell them *to pray God*, tell them *to eat Corn bread*, *Cattle-flesh*, *Milk*, *no eat Man again:* Why then said I to him, *They will kill you*. He look'd grave at that, and then said, *No*, *they no kill me*, *they willing love learn*: He meant by this, they would be willing to learn. He added, they learn'd much of the Bearded-Mans that come in the Boat. Then I ask'd him if he would go back to them? He smil'd at that, and told me he could not swim so far. I told him I would make a *Canoe* for him. He told me, *he would go*, *if I would go with him*. I go! says I, why they will Eat me if I come there? No, no, says he, *me make they no Eat you*; *me make they much Love you:* He meant he would tell them how I had kill'd his Enemies, and sav'd his Life, and so he would make them love me; then he told me as well as he could, how kind they were to seventeen White-men, or Bearded-men, as he call'd them, who came on Shore there in Distress.

From this time I confess I had a Mind to venture over, and see if I could possibly joyn with these Bearded-men, who I made no doubt were *Spaniards* or *Portuguese*; not doubting but if I could we might find some Method to Escape from thence, being upon the Continent, and a good Company together; better than I could from an Island 40 Miles off the Shore, and alone without Help. So after some Days I took *Friday* to work again, by way of Discourse, and told him I would give him a Boat to go back to his own Nation; and accordingly I carry'd him to my Frigate which lay on the other Side of the Island, and having clear'd it of Water, for I always kept it sunk in the Water; I brought it out, shewed it him, and we both went into it.

I found he was a most dextrous Fellow at managing it, would make it go almost as swift and fast again as I could; so when he was in, I said to him, Well now, *Friday*, shall we go to your Nation? He look'd very dull at my saying so, which it seems was, because he thought the Boat too small to go so far. I told him then I had a bigger; so the next Day I went to the Place where the first Boat lay which I had made, but which I could not get into Water: He said that was big enough; but then as I had taken no Care of it, and it had lain two or three and twenty Years there, the Sun had split and dry'd it, that it was in a manner rotten. *Friday* told me such a Boat would do very well, and would carry *much enough Vittle*, *Drink*, *Bread*, that was his Way of Talking.

Upon the whole, I was by this Time so fix'd upon my Design of going over with him to the Continent, that I told him we would go and make one as big as that, and he should go home in it. He answer'd not one Word, but look'd very grave and sad: I ask'd him what was the matter with him? He ask'd me again thus; *Why, you angry mad with* Friday, *what me done?* I ask'd him what he meant; I told him I was not angry with him at all. *No angry! No angry!* says he, repeating the Words several Times, *Why send* Friday *home away to my Nation?* Why, (says I) *Friday*, did you not say you wish'd you were there? *Yes, yes*, says he, *wish be both there, no wish* Friday *there, no Master there.* In a Word, he would not think of going there without me; *I go there!* Friday, (says I) *what shall I do there?* He turn'd very quick upon me at this: *You do great deal much good*, says he, *you teach wild Mans be good sober tame Mans; you tell them know God, pray God, and live new Life. Alas!* Friday, (says I) *thou knowest not what thou sayest, I am but an ignorant Man my self. Yes, yes*, says he, *you teachee me Good, you teachee them Good. No, no*, Friday, (says I) *you shall go without me, leave me here to live by my self, as I did before.* He look'd confus'd again at that Word, and running to one of the Hatchets which he used to wear, he takes it up hastily, comes and gives it me, *What must I do with this?* says I to him. *You take, kill* Friday; (says he.) *What must I kill you for?* said I again. He returns very quick, *What you send* Friday *away for? take, kill* Friday, *no send* Friday *away.* This he spoke so earnestly, that I saw Tears stand in his Eyes: In a Word, I so plainly discover'd the utmost Affection in him to me, and a firm Resolution in him, that I told him then, and often after, that I would never send him away from me, if he was willing to stay with me.

Upon the whole, as I found by all his Discourse a settled Affection to me, and that nothing should part him from me, so I found all the Foundation of his Desire to go to his own Country, was laid in his ardent Affection to the People, and his Hopes of my doing them good; a Thing which as I had no Notion of my self, so I had not the least Thought or Intention, or Desire of undertaking it. But still I found a strong Inclination to my attempting an Escape as above, founded on the Supposition gather'd from the Discourse, (*viz.*) That there were seventeen bearded Men there; and therefore, without any more Delay, I went to Work with *Friday* to find out a great Tree proper to fell, and make a large Periagua or Canoe to undertake the Voyage. There were Trees enough in the Island to have built a little Fleet, not of Periagua's and Canoes, but even of good large Vessels. But the main Thing I look'd at, was to get one so near the Water that we might launch it when it was made, to avoid the Mistake I committed at first.

At last, *Friday* pitch'd upon a Tree, for I found he knew much better than I what kind of Wood was fittest for it, nor can I tell to this Day what Wood to call the Tree we cut down, except that it was very like the Tree we call *Fustic*, or between that and the *Nicaragua* Wood, for it was much of the same Colour and Smell. *Friday* was for burning the Hollow or Cavity of this Tree out to make it for a Boat. But I shew'd him how rather to cut it out with Tools, which, after I had shew'd him how to use, he did very handily, and in about a Month's hard Labour, we finished it, and made it very handsome, especially when with our Axes, which I shew'd him how to handle, we cut and hew'd the out-side into the true Shape of a Boat; after this, however, it cost us near a Fortnight's Time to get her along as it were Inch by Inch upon great Rowlers into the Water. But when she was in, she would have carry'd twenty Men with great Ease.

When she was in the Water, and tho' she was so big, it amazed me to see with what Dexterity and how swift my

Man *Friday* would manage her, turn her, and paddle her along; so I ask'd him if he would, and if we might venture over in her; *Yes*, he said, *he venture over in her very well, tho' great blow Wind*. However, I had a farther Design that he knew nothing of, and that was to make a Mast and Sail and to fit her with an Anchor and Cable: As to a Mast, that was easy enough to get; so I pitch'd upon a strait young Cedar-Tree, which I found near the Place, and which there was great Plenty of in the Island, and I set *Friday* to Work to cut it down, and gave him Directions how to shape and order it. But as to the Sail, that was my particular Care; I knew I had old Sails, or rather Pieces of old Sails enough; but as I had had them now six and twenty Years by me, and had not been very careful to preserve them, not imagining that I should ever have this kind of Use for them, I did not doubt but they were all rotten, and indeed most of them were so; however, I found two Pieces which appear'd pretty good, and with these I went to Work, and with a great deal of Pains, and awkward tedious stitching (you may be sure) for Want of Needles, I at length made a three Corner'd ugly Thing, like what we call in *England*, a Shoulder of Mutton Sail, to go with a Boom at bottom, and a little short Sprit at the Top, such as usually our Ship's Long-Boats sail with, and such as I best knew how to manage; because it was such a one as I had to the Boat, in which I made my Escape from *Barbary*, as related in the first Part of my Story.

I was near two Months performing this last Work, *viz.* rigging and fitting my Mast and Sails; for I finish'd them very compleat, making a small Stay, and a Sail, or Fore-sail to it, to assist, if we should turn to Windward; and which was more than all, I fix'd a Rudder to the Stern of her, to ſteer with; and though I was but a bungling Ship-wright, yet as I knew the Usefulness, and even Necessity of such a Thing, I apply'd my self with so much Pains to do it, that at laſt I brought it to pass; though considering the many dull Contrivances I had for it that fail'd, I think it coſt me almoſt as much Labour as making the Boat.

After all this was done too, I had my Man *Friday* to teach as to what belong'd to the Navigation of my Boat; for though he knew very well how to paddle a *Canoe*, he knew nothing what belong'd to a Sail, and a Rudder; and was the moſt amaz'd, when he saw me work the Boat too and again in the Sea by the Rudder, and how the Sail gyb'd, and fill'd this way, or that way, as the Course we sail'd chang'd; I say, when he saw this, he ſtood like one, aſtonish'd, and amaz'd: However, with a little Use, I made all these Things familiar to him; and he became an expert Sailor, except that as to the Compass, I could make him underſtand very little of that. On the other hand, as there was very little cloudy Weather, and seldom or never any Fogs in those Parts, there was the less occasion for a Compass, seeing the Stars were always to be seen by Night, and the Shore by Day, except in the rainy Seasons, and then no body car'd to ſtir abroad, either by Land or Sea.

I was now entred on the seven and twentieth Year of my Captivity in this Place; though the three laſt Years that I had this Creature with me, ought rather to be left out of the Account, my Habitation being quite of another kind than in all the reſt of the Time. I kept the Anniversary of my landing here with the same Thankfulness to God for his Mercies, as at firſt; and if I had such Cause of Acknowledgment at firſt, I had much more so now, having such additional Testimonies of the Care of Providence over me, and the great Hopes I had of being effectually, and speedily deliver'd; for I had an invincible Impression upon my Thoughts, that my Deliverance was at hand, and that I should not be another Year in this Place: However, I went on with my Husbandry, digging, planting, fencing, as usual; I gather'd and cur'd my Grapes, and did every necessary Thing as before.

The rainy Season was in the mean Time upon me, when I kept more within Doors than at other Times; so I had stow'd our new Vessel as secure as we could, bringing her up into the Creek, where as I said, in the Beginning I landed my Rafts from the Ship, and haling her up to the Shore, at high Water mark, I made my Man *Friday* dig a little Dock, just big enough to hold her, and just deep enough to give her Water enough to float in; and then when the Tide was out, we made a strong Dam cross the End of it, to keep the Water out; and so she lay dry, as to the Tide from the Sea; and to keep the Rain off, we laid a great many Boughs of Trees, so thick, that she was as well thatch'd as a House; and thus we waited for the Month of *November* and *December*, in which I design'd to make my Adventure.

When the settled Season began to come in, as the thought of my Design return'd with the fair Weather, I was preparing daily for the Voyage; and the first Thing I did, was to lay by a certain Quantity of Provisions, being the Stores for our Voyage; and intended in a Week or a Fortnight's Time, to open the Dock, and launch out our Boat. I was busy one Morning upon some Thing of this kind, when I call'd to *Friday*, and bid him go to the Sea Shore, and see if he could find a Turtle, or Tortoise, a Thing which we generally got once a Week, for the Sake of the Eggs, as well as the Flesh: *Friday* had not been long gone, when he came running back, and flew over my outer Wall, or Fence, like one that felt not the Ground, or the Steps he set his Feet on; and before I had time to speak to him, he cries out to me, *O Master! O Master! O Sorrow! O bad!* What's the Matter, *Friday*, says I; *O yonder*, *there*, says he, *one*, *two*, *three Canoe! one*, *two*, *three!* By his way of speaking, I concluded there were six; but on enquiry, I found it was but three: Well, *Friday*, says I, do not be frighted; so I heartned him up as well as I could: However, I saw the poor Fellow was most terribly scar'd; for nothing ran in his Head but that they were come to look for him, and would cut him in Pieces, and eat him; and the poor Fellow trembled so, that I scarce knew what to do with him: I comforted him as well as I could, and told him I was in as much Danger as he, and that they would eat me as well as him; *but*, says I, *Friday*, *we must resolve to fight them*; *Can you fight*, Friday? *Me shoot*, says he, *but there come many great Number*. No matter for that, said I again, our Guns will fright them that we do not kill; so I ask'd him, Whether if I resolv'd to defend him, he would defend me, and stand by me, and do just as I bid him? He said, *Me die*, *when you bid die*, *Master*; so I went and fetch'd a good Dram of Rum, and gave him; for I had been so good a Husband of my Rum, that I had a great deal left: When he had drank it, I made him take the two Fowling-Pieces, which we always carry'd, and load them with large Swan-Shot, as big as small Pistol Bullets; then I took four Muskets, and loaded them with two Slugs, and five small Bullets each; and my two Pistols I loaded with a Brace of Bullets each; I hung my great Sword as usual, naked by my Side, and gave *Friday* his Hatchet.

When I had thus prepar'd my self, I took my Perspective-Glass, and went up to the Side of the Hill, to see what I could discover; and I found quickly, by my Glass, that there were one and twenty Savages, three Prisoners, and three *Canoes*; and that their whole Business seem'd to be the triumphant Banquet upon these three humane Bodies, (a barbarous Feast indeed) but nothing more than as I had observ'd was usual with them.

I observ'd also, that they were landed not where they had done, when *Friday* made his Escape; but nearer to my Creek, where the Shore was low, and where a thick Wood came close almost down to the Sea: This, with the Abhorrence of the inhumane Errand these Wretches came about, fill'd me with such Indignation, that I came down again to *Friday*, and told him, I was resolv'd to go down to them, and kill them all; and ask'd him, If he would stand by me? He was now gotten over his Fright, and his Spirits being a little rais'd, with the Dram I had given him, he was very chearful, and told me, as before, *he would die, when I bid die.*

In this Fit of Fury, I took first and divided the Arms which I had charg'd, as before, between us; I gave *Friday* one Pistol to stick in his Girdle, and three Guns upon his Shoulder; and I took one Pistol, and the other three my self; and in this Posture we march'd out: I took a small Bottle of Rum in my Pocket, and gave *Friday* a large Bag, with more Powder and Bullet; and as to Orders, I charg'd him to keep close behind me, and not to stir, or shoot, or do any Thing, till I bid him; and in the mean Time, not to speak a Word: In this Posture I fetch'd a Compass to my Right-Hand, of near a Mile, as well to get over the Creek, as to get into the Wood; so that I might come within shoot of them, before I should be discover'd, which I had seen by my Glass, it was easy to do.

While I was making this March, my former Thoughts returning, I began to abate my Resolution; I do not mean, that I entertain'd any Fear of their Number; for as they were naked, unarm'd Wretches, 'tis certain I was superior to them; nay, though I had been alone; but it occurr'd to my Thoughts, What Call? What Occasion? much less, What Necessity I was in to go and dip my Hands in Blood, to attack People, who had neither done, or intended me any Wrong? Who as to me were innocent, and whose barbarous Customs were their own Disaster, being in them a Token indeed of God's having left them, with the other Nations of that Part of the World, to such Stupidity, and to such inhumane Courses; but did not call me to take upon me to be a Judge of their Actions, much less an Executioner of his Justice; that whenever he thought fit, he would take the Cause into his own Hands, and by national Vengeance punish them as a People, for national Crimes; but that in the mean time, it was none of my Business; that it was true, *Friday* might justify it, because he was a declar'd Enemy, and in a State of War with those very particular People; and it was lawful for him to attack them; but I could not say the same with respect to me: These Things were so warmly press'd upon my Thoughts, all the way as I went, that I resolv'd I would only go and place my self near them, that I might observe their barbarous Feast, and that I would act then as God should direct; but that unless something offer'd that was more a Call to me than yet I knew of, I would not meddle with them.

With this Resolution I enter'd the Wood, and with all possible Waryness and Silence, *Friday* following close at my Heels, I march'd till I came to the Skirt of the Wood, on the Side which was next to them; only that one Corner of the Wood lay between me and them; here I call'd softly to *Friday*, and shewing him a great Tree, which was just at the Corner of the Wood, I bad him go to the Tree, and bring me Word if he could see there plainly what they were doing; he did so, and came immediately back to me, and told me they might be plainly view'd there; that they were all about their Fire, eating the Flesh of one of their Prisoners; and that another lay bound upon the Sand, a little from them, which he said they would kill next, and which fir'd all the very Soul within me; he told me it was not one of their Nation; but one of the bearded Men, who he had told me of, that came to their Country in the Boat: I was fill'd with Horror at the very naming the white-bearded Man, and going to the Tree, I saw plainly by my Glass, a white Man who lay upon the Beach of the Sea, with his Hands and his Feet ty'd, with Flags, or Things like Rushes; and that he was an *European*, and had Cloaths on.

There was another Tree, and a little Thicket beyond it, about fifty Yards nearer to them than the Place where I was, which by going a little way about, I saw I might come at undiscover'd, and that then I should be within half Shot of them; so I with-held my Passion, though I was indeed enrag'd to the highest Degree, and going back about twenty Paces, I got behind some Bushes, which held all the way, till I came to the other Tree; and then I came to a little rising Ground, which gave me a full View of them, at the Distance of about eighty Yards.

I had now not a Moment to loose; for nineteen of the dreadful Wretches sat upon the Ground, all close huddled together, and had just sent the other two to butcher the poor *Christian*, and bring him perhaps Limb by Limb to their Fire, and they were stoop'd down to untie the

Bands, at his Feet; I turn'd to *Friday*, now *Friday*, said I, do as I bid thee; *Friday* said he would; then *Friday*, says I, do exactly as you see me do, fail in nothing; so I set down one of the Muskets, and the Fowling-Piece, upon the Ground, and *Friday* did the like by his; and with the other Musket, I took my aim at the Savages, bidding him do the like; then asking him, If he was ready? He said, yes, then fire at them, said I; and the same Moment I fir'd also.

Friday took his Aim so much better than I, that on the Side that he shot, he kill'd two of them, and wounded three more; and on my Side, I kill'd one, and wounded two: They were, you may be sure, in a dreadful Consternation; and all of them, who were not hurt, jump'd up upon their Feet, but did not immediately know which way to run, or which way to look: for they knew not from whence their Destruction came: *Friday* kept his Eyes close upon me, that as I had bid him, he might observe what I did; so as soon as the first Shot was made, I threw down the Piece, and took up the Fowling-Piece, and *Friday* did the like; he see me cock, and present, he did the same again; Are you ready? *Friday*, said I; yes, says he; let fly then, says I, in the Name of God, and with that I fir'd again among the amaz'd Wretches, and so did *Friday*; and as our Pieces were now loaden with what I call'd Swan-Shot, or small Pistol Bullets, we found only two drop; but so many were wounded, that they run about yelling, and skreaming, like mad Creatures, all bloody, and miserably wounded, most of them; whereof three more fell quickly after, though not quite dead.

Now *Friday*, says I, laying down the discharg'd Pieces, and taking up the Musket, which was yet loaden; follow me, says I; which he did, with a great deal of Courage;

upon which I rush'd out of the Wood, and shew'd my self, and *Friday* close at my Foot; as soon as I perceiv'd they saw me, I shouted as loud as I could, and bad *Friday* do so too; and running as faſt as I could, *which by the way, was not very faſt, being loaden with Arms as I was*, I made directly towards the poor Victim, who was, as I said, lying upon the Beach, or Shore, between the Place where they sat, and the Sea; the two Butchers who were juſt going to work with him, had left him, at the Suprize of our firſt Fire, and fled in a terrible Fright, to the Sea Side, and had jump'd into a *Canoe*, and three more of the reſt made the same way; I turn'd to *Friday*, and bid him ſtep forwards, and fire at them; he underſtood me immediately, and running about forty Yards, to be near them, he shot at them, and I thought he had kill'd them all; for I see them all fall of a Heap into the Boat; though I saw two of them up again quickly: However, he kill'd two of them, and wounded the third; so that he lay down in the Bottom of the Boat, as if he had been dead.

While my Man *Friday* fir'd at them, I pull'd out my Knife, and cut the Flags that bound the poor Victim, and loosing his Hands, and Feet, I lifted him up, and ask'd him in the *Portuguese* Tongue, What he was? He answer'd in Latin, *Chriſtianus*; but was so weak, and faint, that he could scarce ſtand, or speak; I took my Bottle out of my Pocket, and gave it him, making Signs that he should drink, which he did; and I gave him a Piece of Bread, which he eat; then I ask'd him, What Countryman he was? And he said, *Espagniole*; and being a little recover'd, let me know by all the Signs he could possibly make, how much he was in my Debt for his Deliverance; *Seignior*, said I, with as much *Spanish* as I could make up, we will talk afterwards; but we muſt fight now; if you have any Strength left, take this Piſtol, and Sword, and lay about you; he took them very thankfully, and no sooner had he the Arms in his Hands, but as if they had put new Vigour into him, he flew upon his Murtherers, like a Fury, and had cut two of them in Pieces, in an inſtant; for the Truth is, as the whole was a Surprize to them; so the poor Creatures were so much frighted with the Noise of our Pieces, that they fell down for meer Amazement, and Fear; and had no more Power to attempt their own Escape, than their Flesh had to resiſt our Shot; and that was the Case of those Five that *Friday* shot at in the Boat; for as three of them fell with the Hurt they receiv'd; so the other two fell with the Fright.

I kept my Piece in my Hand ſtill, without firing, being willing to keep my Charge ready; because I had given the *Spaniard* my Piſtol, and Sword; so I call'd to *Friday*, and bad him run up to the Tree, from whence we firſt fir'd, and fetch the Arms which lay there, that had been discharg'd, which he did with great Swiftness; and then giving him my Musket, I sat down my self to load all the reſt again, and bad them come to me when they wanted: While I was loading these Pieces, there happen'd a fierce Engagement between the *Spaniard*, and one of the Savages, who made at him with one of their great wooden Swords, the same Weapon that was to have kill'd him before, if I had not prevented it: The *Spaniard*, who was as bold, and as brave as could be imagin'd, though weak, had fought this *Indian* a good while, and had cut him two great Wounds on his Head; but the Savage being a ſtout luſty Fellow, closing in with him, had thrown him down (being faint) and was wringing my Sword out of his Hand, when the *Spaniard*, tho' undermoſt, wisely quitting the Sword, drew the Piſtol from his Girdle, shot the

Savage through the Body, and kill'd him upon the Spot; before I, who was running to help him, could come near him.

Friday being now left to his Liberty, pursu'd the flying Wretches with no Weapon in his Hand, but his Hatchet; and with that he dispatch'd those three, who, as I said before, were wounded at first and fallen, and all the rest he could come up with, and the *Spaniard* coming to me for a Gun, I gave him one of the Fowling-Pieces, with which he pursu'd two of the Savages, and wounded them both; but as he was not able to run, they both got from him into the Wood, where *Friday* pursu'd them, and kill'd one of them; but the other was too nimble for him, and though he was wounded, yet had plunged himself into the Sea, and swam with all his might off to those two who were left in the *Canoe*, which three in the *Canoe*, with one wounded, who we know not whether he dy'd or no, were all that escap'd our Hands of one and twenty: The Account of the Rest is as follows;

3 Kill'd at our first Shot from the Tree.
2 Kill'd at the next Shot.
2 Kill'd by *Friday* in the Boat.
2 Kill'd by *Ditto*, of those at first wounded.
1 Kill'd by *Ditto*, in the Wood.
3 Kill'd by the *Spaniard*.
4 Kill'd, being found dropp'd here and there of their Wounds, or kill'd by *Friday* in his Chase of them.
4 Escap'd in the Boat, whereof one wounded if not dead.
—
21 In all.
—

Those that were in the *Canoe*, work'd hard to get out of Gun-Shot; and though *Friday* made two or three Shot at them, I did not find that he hit any of them: *Friday* would fain have had me took one of their *Canoes*, and pursu'd them; and indeed I was very anxious about their Escape, least carrying the News home to their People, they should come back perhaps with two or three hundred of their *Canoes*, and devour us by meer Multitude; so I consented to pursue them by Sea, and running to one of their *Canoes*, I jump'd in, and bad *Friday* follow me; but when I was in the *Canoe*, I was surpriz'd to find another poor Creature lye there alive, bound Hand and Foot, as the *Spaniard* was, for the Slaughter, and almost dead with Fear, not knowing what the Matter was; for he had not been able to look up over the Side of the Boat, he was ty'd so hard, Neck and Heels, and had been ty'd so long, that he had really but little Life in him.

I immediately cut the twisted Flags, or Rushes, which they had bound him with, and would have helped him up; but he could not stand, or speak, but groan'd most piteously, believing it seems still that he was only unbound in order to be kill'd.

When *Friday* came to him, I bad him speak to him, and tell him of his Deliverance, and pulling out my Bottle, made him give the poor Wretch a Dram, which, with the News of his being deliver'd, reviv'd him, and he sat up in the Boat; but when *Friday* came to hear him speak, and look in his Face, it would have mov'd any one to Tears, to have seen how *Friday* kiss'd him, embrac'd him, hugg'd him, cry'd, laugh'd, hollow'd, jump'd about, danc'd, sung, then cry'd again, wrung his Hands, beat his own Face, and Head, and then sung, and jump'd about again, like a distracted Creature: It was a good while before I could make him speak to me, or tell me what was the Matter; but when he came a little to himself, he told me, that it was his Father.

It is not easy for me to express how it mov'd me to see what Extasy and filial Affection had work'd in this poor *Savage*, at the Sight of his Father, and of his being deliver'd from Death; nor indeed can I describe half the Extravagancies of his Affection after this; for he went into the Boat and out of the Boat a great many times: When he went in to him, he would sit down by him, open his Breast, and hold his Father's Head close to his Bosom, half an Hour together, to nourish it; then he took his Arms and Ankles, which were numb'd and stiff with the Binding, and chaffed and rubbed them with his Hands; and I perceiving what the Case was, gave him some Rum out of my Bottle, to rub them with, which did them a great deal of Good.

This Action put an End to our Pursuit of the Canoe, with the other *Savages*, who were now gotten almost out of Sight; and it was happy for us that we did not; for it blew so hard within two Hours after, and before they could be gotten a Quarter of their Way, and continued blowing so hard all Night, and that from the *North-west*, which was against them, that I could not suppose their Boat could live, or that they ever reach'd to their own Coast.

But to return to *Friday*, he was so busy about his Father, that I could not find in my Heart to take him off for some time: But after I thought he could leave him a little, I call'd him to me, and he came jumping and laughing, and pleas'd to the highest Extream; then I ask'd him, If he had given his Father any Bread? He shook his Head, and said, *None*: *Ugly Dog eat all up self*; so I gave him a

Cake of Bread out of a little Pouch I carry'd on Purpose; I also gave him a Dram for himself, but he would not taste it, but carry'd it to his Father: I had in my Pocket also two or three Bunches of my Raisins, so I gave him a Handful of them for his Father. He had no sooner given his Father these Raisins, but I saw him come out of the Boat, and run away, as if he had been bewitch'd, he run at such a Rate; for he was the swiftest Fellow of his Foot that ever I saw; I say, he run at such a Rate, that he was out of Sight, as it were, in an instant; and though I call'd, and hollow'd too, after him, it was all one, away he went, and in a Quarter of an Hour, I saw him come back again, though not so fast as he went; and as he came nearer, I found his Pace was slacker, because he had something in his Hand.

When he came up to me, I found he had been quite Home for an Earthen Jugg or Pot to bring his Father some fresh Water, and that he had got two more Cakes, or Loaves of Bread: The Bread he gave me, but the Water he carry'd to his Father: However, as I was very thirsty too, I took a little Sup of it. This Water reviv'd his Father more than all the Rum or Spirits I had given him; for he was just fainting with Thirst.

When his Father had drank, I call'd to him to know if there was any Water left; he said, yes; and I bad him give it to the poor *Spaniard*, who was in as much Want of it as his Father; and I sent one of the Cakes, that *Friday* brought, to the *Spaniard* too, who was indeed very weak, and was reposing himself upon a green Place under the Shade of a Tree; and whose Limbs were also very stiff, and very much swell'd with the rude Bandage he had been ty'd with. When I saw that upon *Friday*'s coming to him with the Water, he sat up and drank, and took the

Bread, and began to eat, I went to him, and gave him a Handful of Raisins; he look'd up in my Face with all the Tokens of Gratitude and Thankfulness, that could appear in any Countenance; but was so weak, notwithstanding he had so exerted himself in the Fight, that he could not stand up upon his Feet; he try'd to do it two or three times, but was really not able, his Ankles were so swell'd and so painful to him; so I bad him sit still, and caused *Friday* to rub his Ankles, and bathe them with Rum, as he had done his Father's.

I observ'd the poor affectionate Creature every two Minutes, or perhaps less, all the while he was here, turn'd his Head about, to see if his Father was in the same Place, and Posture, as he left him sitting; and at last he found he was not to be seen; at which he started up, and without speaking a Word, flew with that Swiftness to him, that one could scarce perceive his Feet to touch the Ground, as he went: But when he came, he only found he had laid himself down to ease his Limbs; so *Friday* came back to me presently, and I then spoke to the *Spaniard* to let *Friday* help him up if he could, and lead him to the Boat, and then he should carry him to our Dwelling, where I would take Care of him: But *Friday*, a lusty strong Fellow, took the *Spaniard* quite up upon his Back, and carry'd him away to the Boat, and set him down softly upon the Side or Gunnel of the Canoe, with his Feet in the inside of it, and then lifted him quite in, and set him close to his Father, and presently stepping out again, launched the Boat off, and paddled it along the Shore faster than I could walk, tho' the Wind blew pretty hard too; so he brought them both safe into our Creek; and leaving them in the Boat, runs away to fetch the other Canoe. As he pass'd me, I spoke to him, and ask'd him, whither he went, he told me, *Go fetch more Boat*; so away he went like the Wind; for sure never Man or Horse run like him, and he had the other Canoe in the Creek, almoſt as soon as I got to it by Land; so he wafted me over, and then went to help our new Gueſts out of the Boat, which he did; but they were neither of them able to walk; so that poor *Friday* knew not what to do.

To remedy this, I went to Work in my Thought, and calling to *Friday* to bid them sit down on the Bank while he came to me, I soon made a Kind of Hand-Barrow to lay them on, and *Friday* and I carry'd them up both together upon it between us: But when we got them to the outside of our Wall or Fortification, we were at a worse Loss than before; for it was impossible to get them over; and I was resolv'd not to break it down: So I set to Work again; and *Friday* and I, in about 2 Hours time, made a very handsom Tent, cover'd with old Sails, and above that with Boughs of Trees, being in the Space without our outward Fence, and between that and the Grove of young Wood which I had planted: And here we made them two Beds of such things as I had (*viz.*) of good Rice-Straw, with Blankets laid upon it to lye on, and another to cover them on each Bed.

My Island was now peopled, and I thought my self very rich in Subjects; and it was a merry Reflection which I frequently made, How like a King I look'd. Firſt of all, the whole Country was my own meer Property; so that I had an undoubted Right of Dominion. 2*dly*, My People were perfectly subjected: I was absolute Lord and Lawgiver; they all owed their Lives to me, and were ready to lay down their Lives, *if there had been Occasion of it*, for me. It was remarkable too, we had but three Subjects, and they were of three different Religions. My Man *Friday* was a Protestant, his Father was a *Pagan* and a *Cannibal*, and the *Spaniard* was a Papist: However, I allow'd Liberty of Conscience throughout my Dominions: But this is by the Way.

As soon as I had secur'd my two weak rescued Prisoners, and given them Shelter, and a Place to rest them upon, I began to think of making some Provision for them: And the first thing I did, I order'd *Friday* to take a yearling Goat, betwixt a Kid and a Goat, out of my particular Flock, to be kill'd, when I cut off the hinder Quarter, and chopping it into small Pieces, I set *Friday* to Work to boiling and stewing, and made them a very good Dish, I assure you, of Flesh and Broth, having put some Barley and Rice also into the Broth; and as I cook'd it without Doors, for I made no Fire within my inner Wall, so I carry'd it all into the new Tent; and having set a Table there for them, I sat down and eat my own Dinner also with them, and, as well as I could, chear'd them and encourag'd them; *Friday* being my Interpreter, especially to his Father, and indeed to the *Spaniard* too; for the *Spaniard* spoke the Language of the *Savages* pretty well.

After we had dined, or rather supped, I order'd *Friday* to take one of the Canoes, and go and fetch our Muskets and other Fire-Arms, which for Want of time we had left upon the Place of Battle, and the next Day I order'd him to go and bury the dead Bodies of the Savages, which lay open to the Sun, and would presently be offensive; and I also ordered him to bury the horrid Remains of their barbarous Feast, which I knew were pretty much, and which I could not think of doing my self; nay, I could not bear to see them, if I went that Way: All which he punctually performed, and defaced the very Appearance of the *Sa-*

vages being there; so that when I went again, I could scarce know where it was, otherwise than by the Corner of the Wood pointing to the Place.

I then began to enter into a little Conversation with my two new Subjects; and first I set *Friday* to enquire of his Father, what he thought of the Escape of the *Savages* in that Canoe, and whether we might expect a Return of them with a Power too great for us to resist: His first Opinion was, that the Savages in the Boat never could live out the Storm which blew that Night they went off, but must of Necessity be drowned or driven *South* to those other Shores, where they were as sure to be devoured as they were to be drowned if they were cast away; but as to what they would do if they came safe on Shore, he said he knew not; but it was his Opinion that they were so dreadfully frighted with the Manner of their being attack'd, the Noise and the Fire, that he believed they would tell their People, they were all kill'd by Thunder and Lightning, not by the Hand of Man, and that the two which appear'd, (*viz.*) *Friday* and me, were two Heavenly Spirits or Furies, come down to destroy them, and not Men with Weapons: This he said he knew, because he heard them all cry out so in their Language to one another, for it was impossible to them to conceive that a Man could dart Fire, and speak Thunder, and kill at a Distance without lifting up the Hand, as was done now: And this old Savage was in the right; for, as I understood since by other Hands, the Savages never attempted to go over to the Island afterwards; they were so terrified with the Accounts given by those four Men, (for it seems they did escape the Sea) that they believ'd whoever went to that enchanted Island would be destroy'd with Fire from the Gods.

This however I knew not, and therefore was under continual Apprehensions for a good while, and kept always upon my Guard, me and all my Army; for as we were now four of us, I would have ventur'd upon a hundred of them fairly in the open Field at any Time.

In a little Time, however, no more Canoes appearing, the Fear of their Coming wore off, and I began to take my former Thoughts of a Voyage to the Main into Consideration, being likewise assur'd by *Friday*'s Father, that I might depend upon good Usage from their Nation on his Account, if I would go.

But my Thoughts were a little suspended, when I had a serious Discourse with the *Spaniard*, and when I understood that there were sixteen more of his Countrymen and *Portuguese*, who having been caſt away, and made their Escape tothat Side, liv'd there at Peace indeed with the Savages, but were very sore put to it for Necessaries, andindeedforLife: I ask'dhim all the Particulars of their Voyage ,and found they were a *Spanish* Ship bound from the *Rio de la Plata* to the *Havana*, being directed to leave their Loading there which was chiefly Hides and Silver, and to bring back what *European* Goods they could meet with there;thatthey had five *Portuguese* Seamen on Board, who they took out of another Wreck; that five of their own Men were drowned when the firſt ship was loſt, and thattheseescapedthro' infinite Dangers and Hazards, and arriv'd almoſt ſtarv'd on the *Cannibal* Coaſt, where they expected to have been devour'd every Moment.

He told me, they had some Arms with them, but they were perfectly useless, for that they had neither Powder or Ball, the Washing of the Sea having spoil'd all their

Powder but a little, which they used at their first Landing to provide themselves some Food.

I ask'd him what he thought would become of them there, and if they had form'd no Design of making any Escape? He said, They had many Consultations about it, but that having neither Vessel, or Tools to build one, or Provisions of any kind, their Councils always ended in Tears and Despair.

I ask'd him how he thought they would receive a Proposal from me, which might tend towards an Escape? And whether, if they were all here, it might not be done? I told him with Freedom, I fear'd mostly their Treachery and ill Usage of me, if I put my Life in their Hands; for that Gratitude was no inherent Virtue in the Nature of Man; nor did Men always square their Dealings by the Obligations they had receiv'd, so much as they did by the Advantages they expected. I told him it would be very hard, that I should be the Instrument of their Deliverance, and that they should afterwards make me their Prisoner in *New Spain*, where an *English* Man was certain to be made a Sacrifice, what Necessity, or what Accident soever, brought him thither: And that I had rather be deliver'd up to the *Savages*, and be devour'd alive, than fall into the merciless Claws of the Priests, and be carry'd into the *Inquisition*. I added, That otherwise I was perswaded, if they were all here, we might, with so many Hands, build a Bark large enough to carry us all away, either to the *Brasils* South-ward, or to the Islands or *Spanish* Coast North-ward: But that if in Requital they should, when I had put Weapons into their Hands, carry me by Force among their own People, I might be ill used for my Kindness to them, and make my Case worse than it was before.

He answer'd with a great deal of Candor and Ingenuity,

That their Condition was so miserable, and they were so sensible of it, that he believed they would abhor the thought of using any Man unkindly that should contribute to their Deliverance; and that, if I pleased, he would go to them with the old Man, and discourse with them about it, and return again, and bring me their Answer: That he would make Conditions with them upon their solemn Oath, That they should be absolutely under my Leading, as their Commander and Captain; and that they should swear upon the Holy Sacraments and the Gospel, to be true to me, and to go to such Christian Country, as that I should agree to, and no other; and to be directed wholly and absolutely by my Orders, 'till they were landed safely in such Country, as I intended; and that he would bring a Contract from them under their Hands for that Purpose.

Then he told me, he would first swear to me himself, That he would never stir from me as long as he liv'd, 'till I gave him Orders; and that he would take my Side to the last Drop of his Blood, if there should happen the least Breach of Faith among his Country-men.

He told me, they were all of them very civil honest Men, and they were under the greatest Distress imaginable, having neither Weapons or Cloaths, nor any Food, but at the Mercy and Discretion of the *Savages*; out of all Hopes of ever returning to their own Country; and that he was sure, if I would undertake their Relief, they would live and die by me.

Upon these Assurances, I resolv'd to venture to relieve them, if possible, and to send the old *Savage* and this *Spaniard* over to them to treat: But when we had gotten all things in a Readiness to go, the *Spaniard* himself started an Objection, which had so much Prudence in it on one hand, and so much Sincerity on the other hand, that I could not but be very well satisfy'd in it; and by his Advice, put off the Deliverance of his Comerades, for at least half a Year. The Case was thus:

He had been with us now about a Month; during which time, I had let him see in what Manner I had provided, with the Assistance of Providence, for my support; and he saw evidently what Stock of Corn and Rice I had laid up; which as it was more than sufficient for myself, so it was not sufficient, at least without good Husbandry, for my Family; now it was encreas'd to Number four: But much less would it be sufficient, if his Countrymen, who were, as he said, fourteen still alive, should come over. And least of all should it be sufficient to victual our Vessel, if we should build one, for a Voyage to any of the Christian Colonies of *America*. So he told me, he thought it would be more advisable, to let him and the two other, dig and cultivate some more Land, as much as I could spare Seed to sow; and that we should wait another Harvest, that we might have a Supply of Corn for his Countrymen when they should come; for Want might be a Temptation to them to disagree, or not to think themselves delivered, otherwise than out of one Difficulty into another. You know, says he, the Children of *Israel*, though they rejoyc'd at first for their being deliver'd out of *Egypt*, yet rebell'd even against God himself that deliver'd them, when they came to want Bread in the Wilderness.

His Caution was so seasonable, and his Advice so good, that I could not but be very well pleased with his Proposal, as well as I was satisfy'd with his Fidelity. So we fell to digging all four of us, as well as the Wooden Tools we were furnish'd with permitted; and in about a Month's time, by the End of which it was Seed time, we had gotten as much Land cur'd and trim'd up, as we sowed 22 Bushels of Barley on, and 16 Jarrs of Rice, which was in short all the Seed we had to spare; nor indeed did we leave our selves Barley sufficient for our own Food, for the six Months that we had to expect our Crop, that is to say, reckoning from the time we set our Seed aside for sowing; for it is not to be supposed it is six Months in the Ground in the Country.

Having now Society enough, and our Number being sufficient to put us out of Fear of the *Savages*, if they had come, unless their Number had been very great, we went freely all over the Island, where-ever we found Occasion; and as here we had our Escape or Deliverance upon our Thoughts, it was impossible, *at least for me*, to have the Means of it out of mine; to this Purpose, I mark'd out several Trees which I thought fit for our Work, and I set *Friday* and his Father to cutting them down; and then I caused the *Spaniard*, to whom I imparted my Thought on that Affair, to oversee and direct their Work. I shewed them with what indefatigable Pains I had hewed a large Tree into single Planks, and I caused them to do the like, till they had made about a Dozen large Planks of good Oak, near 2 Foot broad, 35 Foot long, and from 2 Inches to 4 Inches thick: What prodigious Labour it took up, any one may imagine.

At the same time I contrived to encrease my little Flock of tame Goats as much as I could; and to this Purpose, I made *Friday* and the *Spaniard* go out one Day, and my self with *Friday* the next Day; for we took our Turns: And by this Means we got above 20 young Kids to breed up with the rest; for when-ever we shot the Dam, we saved the Kids, and added them to our Flock: But above all, the Season for curing the Grapes coming on, I caused such a prodigious Quantity to be hung up in the Sun, that I believe, had we been at *Alicant*, where the Raisins of the Sun are cur'd, we could have fill'd 60 or 80 Barrels; and these with our Bread was a great Part of our Food, and very good living too, I assure you; for it is an exceeding nourishing Food.

It was now Harvest, and our Crop in good Order; it was not the most plentiful Encrease I had seen in the Island, but however it was enough to answer our End; for from our 22 Bushels of Barley, we brought in and thrashed out above 220 Bushels; and the like in Proportion of the Rice, which was Store enough for our Food to the next Harvest, tho' all the 16 *Spaniards* had been on Shore with me; or if we had been ready for a Voyage, it would very plentifully have victualled our Ship, to have carry'd us to any Part of the World, that is to say, of *America*.

When we had thus hous'd and secur'd our Magazine of Corn, we fell to Work to make more Wicker Work, (*viz.*) great Baskets in which we kept it; and the *Spaniard* was very handy and dexterous at this Part, and often blam'd me that I did not make some things, for Defence, of this Kind of Work; but I saw no Need of it.

And now having a full Supply of Food for all the Guests I expected, I gave the *Spaniard* Leave to go over to the *Main*, to see what he could do with those he had left behind him there. I gave him a strict Charge in Writing, Not to bring any Man with him, who would not first swear in the Presence of himself and of the old *Savage*, That he would no way injure, fight with, or attack the Person he should find in the Island, who was so kind to send for them in order to their Deliverance; but that they would stand by and defend him against all such Attempts, and where-ever they went, would be entirely under and subjected to his Commands; and that this should be put in Writing, and signed with their Hands: How we were to have this done, when I knew they had neither Pen or Ink; that indeed was a Question which we never asked.

Under these Instructions, the *Spaniard*, and the old *Savage* the Father of *Friday*, went away in one of the Canoes, which they might be said to come in, or rather were brought in, when they came as Prisoners to be devour'd by the *Savages*.

I gave each of them a Musket with a Firelock on it, and about eight Charges of Powder and Ball, charging them to be very good Husbands of both, and not to use either of them but upon urgent Occasion.

This was a chearful Work, being the first Measures used by me in view of my Deliverance for now 27 Years and some Days. I gave them Provisions of Bread, and of dry'd Grapes, sufficient for themselves for many Days, and sufficient for all their Country-men for about eight Days time; and wishing them a good Voyage, I see them go, agreeing with them about a Signal they should hang out at their Return, by which I should know them again, when they came back, at a Distance, before they came on Shore.

They went away with a fair Gale on the Day that the Moon was at Full by my Account, in the Month of *October:* But as for an exact Reckoning of Days, after I had once lost it, I could never recover it again; nor had I kept even the Number of Years so punctually, as to be sure that I was right, tho' as it prov'd, when I afterwards examin'd my Account, I found I had kept a true Reckoning of Years.

It was no less than eight Days I had waited for them, when a strange and unforeseen Accident interven'd, of which the like has not perhaps been heard of in History: I was fast asleep in my Hutch one Morning, when my Man *Friday* came running in to me, and call'd aloud, Master, Master, they are come, they are come.

I jump'd up, and regardless of Danger, I went out, as soon as I could get my Cloaths on, thro' my little Grove, which by the Way was by this time grown to be a very thick Wood; I say, regardless of Danger, I went without my Arms, which was not my Custom to do: But I was surpriz'd, when turning my Eyes to the Sea, I presently saw a Boat at about a league and half's Distance, standing in for the Shore, with a *Shoulder of Mutton Sail*, as they call it; and the Wind blowing pretty fair to bring them in; also I observ'd presently, that they did not come from that Side which the Shore lay on, but from the Southermost End of the Island: Upon this I call'd *Friday* in, and bid him lie close, for these were not the People we look'd for, and that we might not know yet whether they were Friends or Enemies.

In the next Place, I went in to fetch my Perspective Glass, to see what I could make of them; and having taken the Ladder out, I climb'd up to the Top of the Hill, as I used to do when I was apprehensive of any thing, and to take my View the plainer without being discover'd.

I had scarce set my Foot on the Hill, when my Eye plainly discover'd a Ship lying at an Anchor, at about two Leagues and an half's Distance from me South-southeast, but not above a League and an half from the Shore. By my Observation it appear'd plainly to be an English Ship, and the Boat appear'd to be an *English* Long-Boat.

I cannot express the Confusion I was in, tho' the Joy of seeing a Ship, and one who I had Reason to believe was

Mann'd by my own Country-men, and consequently Friends, was such as I cannot describe; but yet I had some secret Doubts hung about me, I cannot tell from whence they came, bidding me keep upon my Guard. In the first Place, it occurr'd to me to consider what Business an *English* Ship could have in that part of the World, since it was not the Way to or from any Part of the World, where the *English* had any Traffick; and I knew there had been no Storms to drive them in there, as in Distress; and that if they were *English* really, it was most probable that they were here upon no good Design; and that I had better continue as I was, than fall into the Hands of Thieves and Murtherers.

Let no Man despise the secret Hints and Notices of Danger, which sometimes are given him, when he may think there is no Possibility of its being real. That such Hints and Notices are given us, I believe few that have made any Observations of things, can deny; that they are certain Discoveries of an invisible World, and a Converse of Spirits, we cannot doubt; and if the Tendency of them seems to be to warn us of Danger, why should we not suppose they are from some friendly Agent, whether supreme, or inferior, and subordinate, is not the Question; and that they are given for our Good?

The present Question abundantly confirms me in the Justice of this Reasoning; for had I not been made cautious by this secret Admonition, come it from whence it will, I had been undone inevitably, and in a far worse Condition than before, as you will see presently.

I had not kept my self long in this Posture, but I saw the Boat draw near the Shore, as if they look'd for a Creek to thrust in at for the Convenience of Landing; however, as they did not come quite far enough, they did not see the little Inlet where I formerly landed my Rafts; but run their Boat on Shore upon the Beach, at about half a Mile from me, which was very happy for me; for otherwise they would have landed just, as I may say, at my Door, and would soon have beaten me out of my Castle, and perhaps have plunder'd me of all I had.

When they were on Shore, I was fully satisfy'd that they were *English* Men; at least, most of them; one or two I thought were *Dutch*; but it did not prove so: There were in all eleven Men, whereof three of them I found were unarm'd, and as I thought, bound; and when the first four or five of them were jump'd on Shore, they took those three out of the Boat as Prisoneers: One of the three I could perceive using the most passionate Gestures of Entreaty, Affliction and Despair, even to a kind of Extravagance; the other two I could perceive lifted up their Hands sometimes, and appear'd concern'd indeed, but not to such a Degree as the first.

I was perfectly confounded at the Sight, and knew not what the meaning of it should be. *Friday* call'd out to me in *English*, as well as he could, *O* Master! *You see* English *Mans eat Prisoner as well as* Savage *Mans*. Why, says I, *Friday*, *Do you think they are a going to eat them then! Yes*, says Friday, *They will eat them: No*, *no*, says I, Friday, *I am afraid they will murther them indeed*, *but you may be sure they will not eat them.*

All this while I had no thought of what the Matter really was; but stood trembling with the Horror of the Sight, expecting every Moment when the three Prisoners should be kill'd; nay, once I saw one of the Villains lift up his Arm with a great Cutlash, as the Seamen call it, or Sword, to strike one of the poor Men; and I expected

An English Ship comes to R. Crusoes Island

to see him fall every Moment, at which all the Blood in my Body seem'd to run chill in my Veins.

I wish'd heartily now for my *Spaniard*, and the *Savage* that was gone with him; or that I had any way to have come undiscover'd within shot of them, that I might have rescu'd the three Men; for I saw no Fire Arms they had among them; but it fell out to my Mind another way.

After I had observ'd the outrageous Usage of the three Men, by the insolent Seamen, I observ'd the Fellows run scattering about the Land, as if they wanted to see the Country: I observ'd that the three other Men had Liberty to go also where they pleas'd; but they sat down all three upon the Ground, very pensive, and look'd like Men in Despair.

This put me in Mind of the first Time when I came on Shore, and began to look about me; How I gave my self over for lost; How wildly I look'd round me: What dreadful Apprehensions I had: And how I lodg'd in the Tree all Night for fear of being devour'd by wild Beasts.

As I knew nothing that night of the Supply I was to receive by the providential Driving of the Ship nearer the Land, by the Storms and Tide, by which I have since been so long nourish'd and supported; so these three poor desolate Men knew nothing how certain of Deliverance and Supply they were, how near it was to them, and how effectually and really they were in a Condition of Safety, at the same Time that they thought themselves lost, and their Case desperate.

So little do we see before us in the World, and so much reason have we to depend chearfully upon the great Maker of the World, that he does not leave his Creatures so absolutely destitute, but that in the worst Circumstances they have always something to be thankful for, and sometimes are nearer their Deliverance than they imagine; nay, are even brought to their Deliverance by the Means by which they seem to be brought to their Destruction.

It was just at the Top of High-Water when these People came on Shore, and while partly they stood parlying with the prisoners they brought, and partly while they rambled about to see what kind of a Place they were in; they had carelessly staid till the Tide was spent, and the Water was ebb'd considerably away, leaving their Boat a-ground.

They had left two Men in the Boat, who as I found afterwards, having drank a little too much Brandy, fell asleep; however, one of them waking sooner than the other, and finding the Boat too fast a-ground for him to stir it, hollow'd for the rest who were straggling about, upon which they all soon came to the Boat; but it was past all their Strength to launch her, the Boat being very heavy, and the Shore on that Side being a soft ousy Sand, almost like a Quick-Sand.

In this Condition, like true Seamen who are perhaps the least of all Mankind given to fore-thought, they gave it over, and away they stroll'd abut the Country again; and I heard one of them say aloud to another, calling them off from the Boat, *Why let her alone*, Jack, *can't ye, she will float next Tide*; by which I was fully confirm'd in the main Enquiry, of what Countrymen they were.

All this while I kept myself very close, not once daring to stir out of my Castle, any farther than to my Place of Observation, near the Top of the Hill; and very glad I was, to think how well it was fortify'd: I knew it was no less than ten Hours before the Boat could be on float again, and by that Time it would be dark, and I might be at more Liberty to see their Motions, and to hear their Discourse, if they had any.

In the mean Time, I fitted my self up for a Battle, as before; though with more Caution, knowing I had to do with another kind of Enemy than I had at first: I order'd *Friday* also, who I had made an excellent Marks-Man with his Gun, to load himself with Arms: I took my self two Fowling-Pieces, and I gave him three Muskets; my Figure indeed was very fierce; I had my formidable Goat-Skin Coat on, with the great Cap I have mention'd, a naked Sword by my Side, two Pistols in my Belt, and a Gun upon each Shoulder.

It was my Design, as I said above, not to have made any Attempt till it was Dark: But about Two a Clock, being the Heat of the Day, I found that in short they were all gone straggling into the Woods, and as I thought were laid down to Sleep. The three poor distressed Men, too Anxious for their Condition to get any Sleep, were however set down under the Shelter of a great Tree, at about a quarter of a Mile from me, and as I thought out of sight of any of the rest.

Upon this I resolv'd to discover my self to them, and learn something of their Condition: Immediately I march'd in the Figure as above, my Man *Friday* at a good Distance behind me, as formidable for his Arms as I, but not making quite so staring a *Spectre-like* Figure as I did.

I came as near them undiscover'd as I could, and then before any of them saw me, I call'd aloud to them in *Spanish*, *What are ye Gentlemen?*

They started up at the Noise, but were ten times more confounded when they saw me, and the uncouth Figure that I made. They made no Answer at all, but I thought I perceiv'd them just going to fly from me, when I spoke to them in *English:* Gentlemen, said I, do not be surpriz'd at me; perhaps you may have a Friend near you when you did not expect it. He must be sent directly from Heaven then, *said one of them very gravely to me, and pulling off his Hat at the same time to me,* for our Condition is past the Help of Man. All Help is from Heaven, *Sir, said I.* But can you put a Stranger in the way how to help you, for you seem to me to be in some great Distress? I saw you when you landed, and when you seem'd to make Applications to the Brutes that came with you, I saw one of them lift up his Sword to kill you.

The poor Man with Tears running down his Face, and trembling, looking like one astonish'd, return'd, *Am I talking to God, or Man! Is it a real Man, or an Angel!* Be in no fear about that, Sir, *said I,* if God had sent an Angel to relieve you, he would have come better Cloath'd, and Arm'd after another manner than you see me in; pray lay aside your Fears, I am a Man, an *English-man,* and dispos'd to assist you, you see; I have one Servant only; we have Arms and Ammunition; tell us freely, Can we serve you? —— What is your Case?

Our Case, said he, Sir, is too long to tell you, while our Murtherers are so near; but in short, Sir, I was Commander of that Ship, my Men have Mutinied against me; they have been hardly prevail'd on not to Murther me, and at last have set me on Shore in this desolate Place, with these two Men with me; one my Mate, the other a Passenger, where we expected to Perish, believing the Place to be uninhabited, and know not yet what to think of it.

Where are those Brutes, your Enemies, said I, do you know where they are gone? *There they lye,* Sir, said he, pointing to a Thicket of Trees; *my Heart trembles, for fear they have seen us, and heard you speak; if they have, they will certainly Murther us all.*

Have they any Fire-Arms, *said I*, He answered they had only two Pieces, and one which they left in the Boat. Well then, said I, leave the reſt to me; I see they are all asleep, it is an easie thing to kill them all; but shall we rather take them Prisoners? He told me there were two desperate Villains among them, that it was scarce safe to shew any Mercy to; but if they were secur'd, he believ'd all the reſt would return to their Duty. I ask'd him, which they were? He told me he could not at that diſtance describe them; but he would obey my Orders in any thing I would direct. Well, says I, let us retreat out of their View or Hearing, leaſt they awake, and we will resolve further; so they willingly went back with me, till the Woods cover'd us from them.

Look you, Sir, said I, if I venture upon your Deliverance, are you willing to make two Conditions with me; he anticipated my Proposals, by telling me, that both he and the Ship, if recover'd, should be wholly Directed and Commanded by me in every thing; and if the Ship was not recover'd, he would live and dye with me in what Part of the World soever I would send him; and the two other Men said the same.

Well, says I, *my Conditions are but two.* 1. That while you ſtay on this Island with me, you will not pretend to any Authority here; and if I put Arms into your Hands, you will upon all Occasions give them up to me, and do no Prejudice to me or mine, upon this Island, and in the mean time be govern'd by my Orders.

2. That if the Ship is, or may be recover'd, you will carry me and my Man to *England* Passage free.

He gave me all the Assurances that the Invention and

Faith of Man could devise, that he would comply with these most reasonable Demands, and besides would owe his Life to me, and acknowledge it upon all Occasions as long as he liv'd.

Well then, *said I*, here are three Muskets for you, with Powder and Ball; tell me next what you think is proper to be done. He shew'd all the Testimony of his Gratitude that he was able; but offer'd to be wholly guided by me. I told him I thought it was hard venturing any thing; but the best Method I could think of was to fire upon them at once, as they lay; and if any was not kill'd at the first Volley, and offer'd to submit, we might save them, and so put it wholly upon God's Providence to direct the Shot.

He said very modestly, that he was loath to kill them, if he could help it, but that those two were incorrigible Villains, and had been the Authors of all the Mutiny in the Ship, and if they escaped, we should be undone still; for they would go on Board, and bring the whole Ship's Company, and destroy us all. *Well then*, says I, *Necessity* legitimates my Advice; for it is the only Way to save our Lives. However, seeing him still cautious of shedding Blood, I told him they should go themselves, and manage as they found convenient.

In the Middle of this Discourse, we heard some of them awake, and soon after, we saw two of them on their Feet. I ask'd him, if either of them were of the Men who he had said were the Heads of the Mutiny? He said, *No:* Well then, said I, you may let them escape, and Providence seems to have wakned them on Purpose to save themselves. Now, says I, if the rest escape you, *it is your Fault*.

Animated with this, he took the Musket, I had given him, in his Hand, and a Pistol in his Belt, and his two Comerades with him, with each Man a Piece in his Hand.

The two Men who were with him, going first, made some Noise, at which one of the Seamen who was awake, turn'd about, and seeing them coming, cry'd out to the rest; but it was too late then; for the Moment he cry'd out, they fir'd; *I mean the two Men*, the Captain wisely reserving his own Piece: They had so well aim'd their Shot at the Men they knew, that one of them was kill'd on the Spot, and the other very much wounded; but not being dead, he started up upon his Feet, and call'd eagerly for help to the other; but the Captain stepping to him, told him, 'twas too late to cry for help, he should call upon God to forgive his Villany, and with that Word knock'd him down with the Stock of his Musket, so that he never spoke more: There were three more in the Company, and one of them was also slightly wounded: By this Time I was come, and when they saw their Danger, and that it was in vain to resist, they begg'd for Mercy: The Captain told them, he would spare their Lives, if they would give him any Assurance of their Abhorrence of the Treachery they had been guilty of, and would swear to be faithful to him in recovering the Ship, and afterwards in carrying her back to *Jamaica*, from whence they came: They gave him all the Protestations of their Sincerity that could be desir'd, and he was willing to believe them, and spare their Lives, which I was not against, only that I oblig'd him to keep them bound Hand and Foot while they were upon the Island.

While this was doing, I sent *Friday* with the Captain's Mate to the Boat, with orders to secure her, and bring away the Oars, and Sail, which they did; and by and by, three straggling Men that were (happily for them) parted from the rest, came back upon hearing the Guns fir'd, and seeing their Captain, who before was their Prisoner, now their Conqueror, they submitted to be bound also; and so our Victory was compleat.

It now remain'd, that the Captain and I should enquire into one another's Circumstances: I began first, and told him my whole History, which he heard with an Attention even to Amazement; and particularly, at the wonderful Manner of my being furnish'd with Provisions and Ammunition; and indeed, as my Story is a whole Collection of Wonders, it affected him deeply; but when he reflected from thence upon himself, and how I seem'd to have been preserv'd there, on purpose to save his Life, the Tears ran down his Face, and he could not speak a Word more.

After this Communication was at an End, I carry'd him and his two Men into my Apartment, leading them in, just where I came out, *viz.* At the Top of the House, where I refresh'd them with such Provisions as I had, and shew'd them all the Contrivances I had made, during my long, long, inhabiting that Place.

All I shew'd them, all I said to them, was perfectly amazing; but above all, the Captain admir'd my Fortification, and how perfectly I had conceal'd my Retreat with a Grove of Trees, which having been now planted near twenty Years, and the Trees growing much faster than in *England*, was become a little Wood, and so thick, that it was unpassable in any Part of it, but at that one Side, where I had reserv'd my little winding Passage into it: I told him, this was my Castle, and my Residence; but that I had a Seat in the Country, as most Princes have, whither I could retreat upon Occasion, and I would shew him that too another Time; but at present, our Business was to consider how to recover the Ship: He agreed with me as to that; but told me, he was perfectly at a Loss what Measures to take; for that there were still six and twenty

Hands on board, who having entred into a cursed Conspiracy, by which they had all forfeited their Lives to the Law, would be harden'd in it now by Desperation; and would carry it on, knowing that if they were reduc'd, they should be brought to the Gallows, as soon as they came to *England*, or to any of the *English* Colonies; and that therefore there would be no attacking them, with so small a Number as we were.

I mus'd for some Time upon what he had said, and found it was a very rational Conclusion; and that therefore something was to be resolv'd on very speedily, as well to draw the Men on board into some Snare for their Surprize, as to prevent their Landing upon us, and destroying us; upon this it presently occurr'd to me, that in a little while the Ship's Crew wondring what was become of their Comrades, and of the Boat, would certainly come on Shore in their other Boat, to see for them, and that then perhaps they might come arm'd, and be too strong for us; this he allow'd was rational.

Upon this, I told him the first Thing we had to do, was to stave the Boat, which lay upon the Beach, so that they might not carry her off; and taking every Thing out of her, leave her so far useless as not to be fit to swim; accordingly we went on board, took the Arms which were left on board, out of her, and whatever else we found there, which was a Bottle of Brandy, and another of Rum, a few Bisket Cakes, a Horn of Powder, and a great Lump of Sugar, in a Piece of Canvas; the Sugar was five or six Pounds, all which was very welcome to me, especially the Brandy, and Sugar, of which I had had none left for many Years.

When we had carry'd all these Things on Shore (the Oars, Mast, Sail, and Rudder of the Boat, were carry'd away before, as above) we knock'd a great Hole in her Bottom, that if they had come strong enough to master us, yet they could not carry off the Boat.

Indeed, it was not much in my Thoughts, that we could be able to recover the Ship; but my View was that if they went away without the Boat, I did not much question to make her fit again, to carry us away to the *Leeward* Islands, and call upon our Friends, the *Spaniards*, in my Way, for I had them still in my Thoughts.

While we were thus preparing our Designs, and had first, by main Strength heav'd the Boat up upon the Beach, so high that the Tide would not fleet her off at High-Water-Mark; and besides, had broke a Hole in her Bottom, too big to be quickly stopp'd, and were sat down musing what we should do; we heard the Ship fire a Gun, and saw her make a Waft with her Antient, as a Signal for the Boat to come on board; but no Boat stirr'd; and they fir'd several Times, making other Signals for the Boat.

At last, when all their Signals and Firing prov'd fruitless, and they found the Boat did not stir, we saw them by the Help of my Glasses, hoist another Boat out, and row towards the Shore; and we found as they approach'd that there was no less than ten Men in her, and that they had Fire-Arms with them.

As the Ship lay almost two Leagues from the Shore, we had a full View of them as they came, and a plain Sight of the Men even of their Faces, because the Tide having set them a little to the *East* of the other Boat, they row'd up under Shore, to come to the same Place, where the other had landed, and where the Boat lay.

By this Means, I say, we had a full View of them, and the Captain knew the Persons and Characters of all the Men in the Boat, of whom he said, that there were three very honeſt Fellows, who he was sure were led into this Conspiracy by the reſt, being over-power'd and frighted.

But that as for the Boatswain, who it seems was the chief Officer among them, and all the reſt, they were as outragious as any of the Ship's Crew, and were no doubt made desperate in their new Enterprize, and terribly apprehensive he was, that they would be too powerful for us.

I smil'd at him, and told him, that Men in our Circumſtances were paſt the Operation of Fear: That seeing almoſt every Condition that could be, was better than that which we were suppos'd to be in, we ought to expect that the Consequence, whether Death or Life, would be sure to be a Deliverance: I ask'd him, What he thought of the Circumſtances of my Life? And, Whether a Deliverance were not worth venturing for? And where, Sir, said I, is your Belief of my being preserv'd here on purpose to save your Life, which elevated you a little while ago? For my Part, said I, there seems to be but one Thing amiss in all the Prospect of it; *What's that?* Says he; why, said I, 'Tis, that as you say, there are three or four honeſt Fellows among them, which should be spar'd; had they been all of the wicked Part of the Crew, I should have thought God's Providence had singled them out to deliver them into your Hands; for depend upon it, every Man of them that comes a-shore are our own, and shall die, or live, as they behave to us.

As I spoke this with a rais'd Voice and chearful Countenance, I found it greatly encourag'd him; so we set vigorously to our Business: We had upon the firſt Appearance of the Boat's coming from the Ship, consider'd of separating our Prisoners, and had indeed secur'd them effectually.

Two of them, of whom the Captain was less assur'd

than ordinary, I sent with *Friday*, and one of the three (deliver'd Men) to my Cave, where they were remote enough, and out of Danger of being heard or discover'd, or of finding their way out of the Woods, if they could have deliver'd themselves: Here they left them bound, but gave them Provisions, and promis'd them if they continu'd there quietly, to give them their Liberty in a Day or two; but that if they attempted their Escape, they should be put to Death without Mercy: They promis'd faithfully to bear their Confinement with Patience, and were very thankful that they had such good Usage, as to have Provisions, and a Light left them; for *Friday* gave them Candles (such as we made our selves) for their Comfort; and they did not know but that he stood Sentinel over them at the Entrance.

The other Prisoners had better Usage; two of them were kept pinion'd indeed, because the Captain was not free to trust them; but the other two were taken into my Service upon their Captain's Recommendation, and upon their solemnly engaging to live and die with us; so with them and the three honest Men, we were seven Men, well arm'd; and I made no doubt we shou'd be able to deal well enough with the Ten that were a coming, considering that the Captain had said, there were three or four honest Men among them also.

As soon as they got to the Place where their other Boat lay, they run their Boat in to the Beach, and came all on Shore, haling the Boat up after them, which I was glad to see; for I was afraid they would rather have left the Boat at an Anchor, some Distance from the Shore, with some Hands in her, to guard her; and so we should not be able to seize the Boat.

Being on Shore, the first Thing they did, they ran all

to their other Boat, and it was easy to see that they were under a great Surprize, to find her ſtripp'd as above, of all that was in her, and a great hole in her Bottom.

After they had mus'd a while upon this, they set up two or three great Shouts, hollowing with all their might, to try if they could make their Companions hear; but all was to no purpose: Then they came all close in a Ring, and fir'd a Volley of their small Arms, which indeed we heard, and the Ecchos made the Woods ring; but it was all one, those in the Cave we were sure could not hear, and those in our keeping, though they heard it well enough, yet durſt give no Answer to them.

They were so aſtonish'd at the Surprize of this, that as they told us afterwards, they resolv'd to go all on board again to their Ship, and let them know, that the Men were all murther'd, and the Long-Boat ſtav'd; accordingly they immediately launch'd their Boat again, and gat all of them on board.

The Captain was terribly amaz'd, and even confounded at this, believing they would go on board the Ship again, and set Sail, giving their Comrades for loſt, and so he should ſtill lose the Ship, which he was in Hopes we should have recover'd; but he was quickly as much frighted the other way.

They had not been long put off with the Boat, but we perceiv'd them all coming on Shore again; but with this new Measure in their Conduct, which it seems they consulted together upon, *viz.* To leave three Men in the Boat, and the reſt to go on Shore, and go up into the Country to look for their Fellows.

This was a great Disappointment to us; for now we were at a Loss what to do; for our seizing those seven Men on Shore would be no Advantage to us, if we let the

Boat escape; because they would then row away to the Ship, and then the rest of them would be sure to weigh and set Sail, and so our recovering the Ship would be lost.

However, we had no Remedy, but to wait and see what the Issue of Things might present; the seven Men came on Shore, and the three who remain'd in the Boat, put her off to a good Distance from the Shore, and came to an Anchor to wait for them; so that it was impossible for us to come at them in the Boat.

Those that came on Shore, kept close together, marching towards the Top of the little Hill, under which my Habitation lay; and we could see them plainly, though they could not perceive us: We could have been very glad they would have come nearer to us, so that we might have fir'd at them, or that they would have gone farther off, that we might have come abroad.

But when they were come to the Brow of the Hill, where they could see a great way into the Valleys and Woods, which lay towards the *North-East* Part, and where the Island lay lowest, they shouted, and hollow'd, till they were weary; and not caring it seems to venture far from the Shore, nor far from one another, they sat down together under a Tree, to consider of it: Had they thought fit to have gone to sleep there, as the other Party of them had done, they had done the Jobb for us; but they were too full of Apprehensions of Danger, to venture to go to sleep, though they could not tell what the Danger was they had to fear neither.

The Captain made a very just Proposal to me, upon this Consultation of theirs, *viz.* That perhaps they would all fire a Volley again, to endeavour to make their Fellows hear and that we should all Sally upon them, just at the

Juncture when their Pieces were all discharg'd, and they would certainly yield, and we should have them without Blood-shed: I lik'd the Proposal, provided it was done while we were near enough to come up to them, before they could load their Pieces again.

But this Event did not happen, and we lay still a long Time, very irresolute what Course to take; at length I told them, there would be nothing to be done in my Opinion till Night, and then if they did not return to the Boat, perhaps we might find a way to get between them, and the Shore, and so might use some Stratagem with them in the Boat, to get them on Shore.

We waited a great while, though very impatient for their removing; and were very uneasy, when after long Consultations, we saw them start all up, and march down toward the Sea: It seems they had such dreadful Apprehensions upon them, of the Danger of the Place, that they resolv'd to go on board the Ship again, give their Companions over for lost, and so go on with their intended Voyage with the Ship.

As soon as I perceiv'd them go towards the Shore, I imagin'd it to be as it really was, That they had given over their Search, and were for going back again; and the Captain, as soon as I told him my Thoughts, was ready to sink at the Apprehensions of it, but I presently thought of a Stratagem to fetch them back again, and which answer'd my End to a Tittle.

I order'd *Friday*, and the Captain's Mate, to go over the little Creek *Westward*, towards the Place were the *Savages* came on Shore, when *Friday* was rescu'd; and as soon as they came to a little rising Ground, at about half a Mile Distance, I bad them hollow, as loud as they could, and wait till they found the Seamen heard them; that as soon as ever they heard the Seamen answer them, they should return it again, and then keeping out of Sight, take a round, always answering when the other hollow'd, to draw them as far into the Island, and among the Woods, as possible, and then wheel about again to me, by such ways as I directed them.

They were just going into the Boat, when *Friday* and the Mate hollow'd, and they presently heard them, and answering, run along the Shore *Westward*, towards the Voice they heard, where they were presently stopp'd by the Creek, where the Water being up, they could not get over, and call'd for the Boat to come up, and set them over, as indeed I expected.

When they had set themselves over, I observ'd, that the Boat being gone up a good way into the Creek, and as it were, in a Harbour within the Land, they took one of the three Men out of her to go along with them, and left only two in the Boat, having fastned her to the Stump of a little Tree on the Shore.

This was what I wish'd for, and immediately leaving *Friday* and the Captain's Mate to their Business, I took the rest with me, and crossing the Creek out of their Sight, we surpriz'd the two Men before they were aware; one of them lying on Shore, and the other being in the Boat; the Fellow on Shore, was between sleeping and waking, and going to start up, the Captain who was foremost, ran in upon him, and knock'd him down, and then call'd out to him in the Boat, to yield, or he was a dead Man.

There needed very few Arguments to perswade a single Man to yield, when he saw five Men upon him, and his Comrade knock'd down; besides, this was it seems one of the three who were not so hearty in the Mutiny as the rest of the Crew, and therefore was easily perswaded, not only to yield, but afterwards to joyn very sincerely with us.

In the mean time, *Friday* and the Captain's Mate so well manag'd their Business with the reſt, that they drew them by hollowing and answering, from one Hill to another, and from one Wood to another, till they not only heartily tyr'd them, but left them, where they were very sure they could not reach back to the Boat, before it was dark; and indeed they were heartily tyr'd themselves also by the Time they came back to us.

We had nothing now to do, but to watch for them, in the Dark, and to fall upon them, so as to make sure work with them.

It was several Hours after *Friday* came back to me, before they came back to their Boat; and we could hear the foremoſt of them long before they came quite up, calling to those behind to come along, and could also hear them answer and complain, how lame and tyr'd they were, and not able to come any faſter, which was very welcome News to us.

At length they came up to the Boat; but 'tis impossible to express their Confusion, when they found the Boat faſt a-Ground in the Creek, the Tide ebb'd out, and their two Men gone: We could hear them call to one another in a moſt lamentable Manner, telling one another, they were gotten into an inchanted Island; that either there were Inhabitants in it, and they should all be murther'd, or else there were Devils and Spirits in it, and they should be all carry'd away, and devour'd.

They hallow'd again, and call'd their two Comerades by their Names, a great many times, but no Answer. After some time, we could see them, by the little Light there was, run about wringing their Hands like Men in De-pair; and that sometimes they would go and sit down in the Boat to rest themselves, then come ashore again, and walk about again, and so over the same thing again.

My Men would fain have me give them Leave to fall upon them at once in the Dark; but I was willing to take them at some Advantage, so to spare them, and kill as few of them as I could; and especially I was unwilling to hazard the killing any of our own Men, knowing the other were very well armed. I resolved to wait to see if they did not separate; and therefore to make sure of them, I drew my Ambuscade nearer, and order'd *Friday* and the Captain, to creep upon their Hands and Feet as close to the Ground as they could, that they might not be discover'd, and get as near them as they could possibly, before they offered to fire.

They had not been long in that Posture, but that the Boatswain, who was the principal Ringleader of the Mutiny, and had now shewn himself the most dejected and dispirited of all the rest, came walking towards them with two more of their Crew; the Captain was so eager, as having this principal Rogue so much in his Power, that he could hardly have Patience to let him come so near, as to be sure of him; for they only heard his Tongue before: But when they came nearer, the Captain and *Friday* starting up on their Feet, let fly at them.

The Boatswain was kill'd upon the Spot, the next Man was shot into the Body, and fell just by him, tho' he did not die 'till an Hour or two after; and the third run for it.

At the Noise of the Fire, I immediately advanc'd with my whole Army, which was now 8 men, *viz.* my self *Generalissimo*, *Friday* my Lieutenant-General, the Captain and his two Men, and the three Prisoners of War, who we had trusted with Arms.

We came upon them indeed in the Dark, so that they could not see our Number; and I made the Man we had left in the Boat, who was now one of us, call to them by Name, to try if I could bring them to a Parley, and so might perhaps reduce them to Terms, which fell out just as we desir'd: for indeed it was easy to think, as their Condition then was, they would be very willing to capitulate; so he calls out as loud as he could, to one of them, *Tom Smith*, *Tom Smith; Tom Smith* answered immediately, *Who's that*, Robinson? for it seems he knew his Voice: T'other answered, *Ay, ay; for God's Sake*, Tom Smith, *throw down your Arms, and yield*, or, *you are all dead Men this Moment.*

Who must we yield to? where are they? (says *Smith* again;) *Here they are*, says he, here's our Captain, and fifty Men with him, have been hunting you this two Hours; the Boatswain is kill'd, *Will Frye* is wounded, and I am a Prisoner; and if you do not yield, you are all lost.

Will they give us Quarter then, (says *Tom Smith*) and we will yield? *I'll go and ask, if you promise to yield*, says *Robinson*; so he ask'd the Captain, and the Captain then calls himself out, You *Smith*, you know my Voice, if you lay down your Arms immediately, and submit, you shall have your Lives all but *Will. Atkins.*

Upon this, *Will Atkins* cry'd out, *For God's sake, Captain, give me Quarter, what have I done? They have been all as bad as I*; which by the Way was not true neither; for it seems this *Will. Atkins* was the first Man that laid hold of the Captain, when they first mutiny'd, and used him barbarously, in tying his Hands, and giving him injurious Language. However, the Captain told him he must lay down his Arms at Discretion, and trust to the Governour's

Mercy, by which he meant me; for they all call'd me Governour.

In a Word, they all laid down their Arms, and begg'd their Lives; and I sent the Man that had parley'd with them, and two more, who bound them all; and then my great Army of 50 Men, which particularly with those three, were all but eight, came up and seiz'd upon them all, and upon their Boat, only that I kept my self and one more out of Sight, for Reasons of State.

Our next Work was to repair the Boat, and think of seizing the Ship; and as for the Captain, now he had Leisure to parley with them: He expostulated with them upon the Villany of their Practices with him, and at length upon the farther Wickedness of their Design, and how certainly it must bring them to Misery and Distress in the End, and perhaps to the Gallows.

They all appear'd very penitent, and begg'd hard for their Lives; as for that, he told them, they were none of his Prisoners, but the Commander's of the Island; that they thought they had set him on Shore in a barren uninhabitated Island, but it had pleased God so to direct them, that the Island was inhabited, and that the Governour was an *English* Man; that he might hang them all there, if he pleased; but as he had given them all Quarter, he supposed he would send them to *England* to be dealt with there, as Justice requir'd, except *Atkins*, who he was commanded by the Governour to advise to prepare for Death; for that he would be hang'd in the Morning.

Though this was all a Fiction of his own, yet it had its desired Effect; *Atkins* fell upon his Knees to beg the Captain to interceed with the Governour for his Life; and all the rest beg'd of him for God's sake, that they might not be sent to *England*.

It now occurr'd to me, that the time of our Deliverance was come, and that it would be a most easy thing to bring these Fellows in, to be hearty in getting Possession of the Ship; so I retir'd in the Dark from them, that they might not see what Kind of a Governour they had, and call'd the Captain to me; when I call'd, as at a good Distance, one of the Men was order'd to speak again, and say to the Captain, *Captain, the Commander calls for you*; and presently the Captain reply'd, *Tell his Excellency, I am just a coming*: This more perfectly amused them; and they all believed that the Commander was just by with his fifty Men.

Upon the Captain's coming to me, I told him my Project for seizing the Ship, which he lik'd of wonderfully well, and resolv'd to put it in Execution the next Morning.

But in Order to execute it with more Art, and secure of Success, I told him, we must divide the Prisoners, and that he should go and take *Atkins* and two more of the worst of them, and send them pinion'd to the Cave where the others lay: This was committed to *Friday* and the two Men who came on Shore with the Captain.

They convey'd them to the Cave, as to a Prison; and it was indeed a dismal Place, especially to Men in their Condition.

The other I order'd to my *Bower*, as I call'd it, of which I have given a full Description; and as it was fenc'd in, and they pinion'd, the Place was secure enough, considering they were upon their Behaviour.

To these in the Morning I sent the Captain, who was to enter into a Parley with them, in a Word, to try them, and tell me, whether he thought they might be trusted or no, to go on Board and surprize the Ship. He talk'd to them of the Injury done him; of the Condition they were brought to; and that though the Governour had given them Quarter for their Lives, as to the present Action, yet that if they were sent to *England*, they would all be hang'd in Chains, to be sure; but that if they would join in so just an Attempt, as to recover the Ship, he would have the Governour's engagement for their Pardon.

Any one may guess how readily such a Proposal would be accepted by Men in their Condition; they fell down on their Knees to the Captain, and promised with the deepest Imprecations, that they would be faithful to him to the last Drop, and that they should owe their Lives to him, and would go with him all over the World, that they would own him for a Father to them as long as they liv'd.

Well, says the Captain, I must go and tell the Governour what you say, and see what I can do to bring him to consent to it: So he brought me an Account of the Temper he found them in; and that he verily believ'd they would be faithful.

However, that we might be very secure, I told him he should go back again, and choose out those five and tell them, they might see that he did not want Men, that he would take out those five to be his Assistants, and that the Governour would keep the other two, and the three that were sent Prisoners to the Castle, (*my Cave*) as Hostages, for the Fidelity of those five; and that if they prov'd unfaithful in the Execution, the five Hostages should be hang'd in Chains alive upon the Shore.

This look'd severe, and convinc'd them that the Governour was in Earnest; however they had no Way left them, but to accept it; and it was now the Business of the Prisoners, as much as of the Captain, to perswade the other five to do their Duty.

Our Strength was now thus ordered for the Expedition: 1. The Captain, his Mate, and Passenger. 2. Then the two Prisoners of the first Gang, to whom having their Characters from the Captain, I had given their Liberty, and trusted them with Arms. 3. The other two who I had kept till now, in my Bower, pinion'd; but upon the Captain's Motion, had now releas'd. 4. These five releas'd at last: So that they were twelve in all, besides five we kept Prisoners in the Cave, for Hostages.

I ask'd the Captain, if he was willing to venture with these Hands on Board the Ship; for as for me and my Man *Friday*, I did not think it was proper for us to stir, having seven Men left behind; and it was Employment enough for us to keep them assunder, and supply them with Victuals.

As to the five in the Cave, I resolv'd to keep them fast, but *Friday* went in twice a Day to them, to supply them with Necessaries; and I made the other two carry Provisions to a certain Distance, where *Friday* was to take it.

When I shew'd my self to the two Hostages, it was with the Captain, who told them, I was the Person the Governour had order'd to look after them, and that it was the Governour's Pleasure they should not stir any where, but by my Direction; that if they did, they should be fetch'd into the Castle, and be lay'd in Irons; so that as we never suffered them to see me as Governour, so I now appear'd as another Person, and spoke of the Governour, the Garrison, the Castle, and the like, upon all Occasions.

The Captain now had no Difficulty before him, but to furnish his two Boats, stop the Breach of one, and Man them. He made his Passenger Captain of one, with four other Men; and himself, and his Mate, and five more, went in the other: And they contriv'd their Business very well; for they came up to the Ship about Midnight: As soon as they came within Call of the Ship, he made *Robinson* hale them, and tell them they had brought off the Men and the Boat, but that it was a long time before they had found them, and the like; holding them in a Chat 'till they came to the Ship's Side; when the Captain and the Mate entring first with their Arms, immediately knock'd down the second Mate and Carpenter, with the But-end of their Muskets, being very faithfully seconded by their Men; they secur'd all the rest that were upon the Main and Quarter Decks, and began to fasten the Hatches to keep them down who were below, when the other Boat and their Men entring at the fore Chains, secur'd the Fore-Castle of the Ship, and the Scuttle which went down into the Cook-Room, making three Men they found there, Prisoners.

When this was done, and all safe upon Deck, the Captain order'd the Mate with three Men to break into the Round-House where the new Rebel Captain lay, and having taken the Alarm, was gotten up, and with two Men and a Boy had gotten Fire Arms in their Hands; and when the Mate with a Crow split open the Door, the new Captain and his Men fir'd boldly among them, and wounded the Mate with a Musket Ball, which broke his Arm, and wounded two more of the Men but kill'd no Body.

The Mate calling for Help, rush'd however into the Round-House, wounded as he was, and with his Pistol shot the new Captain thro' the Head, the Bullet entring at his Mouth, and came out again behind one of his Ears; so that he never spoke a Word; upon which the rest yielded, and the Ship was taken effectually, without any more Lives lost.

R. Crusoe recovers the Ship for the Captn and Conquers the Pyrates

As soon as the Ship was thus secur'd, the Captain order'd seven Guns to be fir'd, which was the Signal agreed upon with me, to give me Notice of his Success, which you may be sure I was very glad to hear, having sat watching upon the Shore for it till near two of the Clock in the Morning.

Having thus heard the Signal plainly, I laid me down; and it having been a Day of great Fatigue to me, I slept very sound, 'till I was something surpriz'd with the Noise of a Gun; and presently starting up, I heard a Man call me by the Name of Governour, Governour, and presently I knew the Captain's Voice, when climbing up to the Top of the Hill, there he stood, and pointing to the Ship, he embrac'd me in his Arms, *My dear Friend and Deliverer*, says he, *there's your Ship, for she is all yours, and so are we and all that belong to her*. I cast my Eyes to the Ship, and there she rode within little more than half a Mile of the Shore; for they had weighed her Anchor as soon as they were Masters of her; and the Weather being fair, had brought her to an Anchor just against the Mouth of the little Creek; and the Tide being up, the Captain had brought the Pinnace in near the Place where I at first landed my Rafts, and so landed just at my Door.

I was at first ready to sink down with the Surprize. For I saw my Deliverance indeed visibly put into my hands, all things easy, and a large Ship just ready to carry me away whither I pleased to go. At first, for some time, I was not able to answer him one Word; but as he had taken me in his Arms, I held fast by him, or I should have fallen to the Ground.

He perceived the Surprize, and immediately pulls a Bottle out of his Pocket, and gave me a Dram of Cordial, which he had brought on Purpose for me; after I had drank it, I sat down upon the Ground; and though it brought me to my self, yet it was a good while before I could speak a Word to him.

All this while the poor Man was in as great an Extasy as I, only not under any Surprize, as I was; and he said a thousand kind tender things to me, to compose me and bring me to my self; but such was the Flood of Joy in my Breast, that it put all my Spirits into Confusion; at last it broke out into Tears, and in a little while after, I recovered my Speech.

Then I took my Turn, and embrac'd him as my Deliverer; and we rejoyc'd together. I told him, I look'd upon him as a Man sent from Heaven to deliver me, and that the whole Transaction seemed to be a Chain of Wonders; that such things as these were the Testimonies we had of a secret Hand of Providence governing the World, and an Evidence, that the Eyes of an infinite Power could search into the remotest Corner of the World, and send Help to the Miserable whenever he pleased.

I forgot not to lift up my Heart in Thankfulness to Heaven; and what Heart could forbear to bless him, who had not only in a miraculous Manner provided for one in such a Wilderness, and in such a desolate Condition, but from whom every Deliverance must always be acknowledged to proceed.

When we had talk'd a while, the Captain told me, he had brought me some little Refreshment, such as the Ship afforded, and such as the Wretches that had been so long his Master had not plunder'd him of: Upon this he call'd aloud to the Boat, and bid his Men bring the things ashore that were for the Governour; and indeed it was a Present, as if I had been one not that was to be carry'd away along with them, but as if I had been to dwell upon the Island still, and they were to go without me.

First he had brought me a Case of Bottles full of excellent Cordial Waters, six large Bottles of *Madera* Wine; the Bottles held two Quarts a-piece; two Pound of excellent good Tobacco, twelve good Pieces of the Ship's Beef, and six Pieces of Pork, with a Bag of Pease, and about a hundred Weight of Bisket.

He brought me also a Box of Sugar, a Box of Flower, a Bag full of Lemons, and two Bottles of Lime-Juice, and Abundance of other things: But besides these, and what was a thousand times more useful to me, he brought me six clean new Shirts, six very good Neckcloaths, two Pair of Gloves, one Pair of Shoes, a Hat, and one Pair of Stockings, and a very good Suit of Cloaths of his own, which had been worn but very little: In a Word, he cloathed me from Head to Foot.

It was a very kind and agreeable Present, as any one may imagine to one in my Circumstances: But never was any thing in the World of that Kind so unpleasant, awkard, and uneasy, as it was to me to wear such Cloaths at their first putting on.

After these Ceremonies past, and after all his good things were brought into my little Apartment, we began to consult what was to be done with the Prisoners we had; for it was worth considering, whether we might venture to take them away with us or no, especially two of them, who we knew to be incorrigible and refractory to the last Degree; and the Captain said, he knew they were such Rogues, that there was no obliging them, and if he did carry them away, it must be in Irons, as Malefactors to be delivered over to Justice at the first *English* Colony he could come at; and I found that the Captain himself was very anxious about it.

Upon this, I told him, that if he desir'd it, I durst undertake to bring the two Men he spoke of, to make it their own Request that he should leave them upon the Island: *I should be very glad of that*, says the Captain, *with all my Heart*.

Well, says I, I will send for them up, and talk with them for you; so I caused *Friday* and the two Hostages, for they were now discharg'd, their Comrades having perform'd their Promise; I say, I caused them to go to the Cave, and bring up the five Men pinion'd, as they were, to the Bower, and keep them there 'till I came.

After some time, I came thither dress'd in my new Habit, and now I was call'd Governour again; being all met, and the Captain with me, I caused the Men to be brought before me, and I told them, I had had a full Account of their villanous Behaviour to the Captain, and how they had run away with the Ship, and were preparing to commit farther Robberies, but that Providence had ensnar'd them in their own Ways, and that they were fallen into the Pit which they had digged for others.

I let them know, that by my Direction the Ship had been seiz'd, that she lay now in the Road; and they might see by and by, that their new Captain had receiv'd the Reward of his Villany; for that they might see him hanging at the Yard-Arm.

That as to them, I wanted to know what they had to say, why I should not execute them as Pirates taken in the Fact, as by my Commission they could not doubt I had Authority to do.

One of them answer'd in the Name of the rest, That they had nothing to say but this, That when they were taken, the Captain promis'd them their Lives, and they humbly implor'd my Mercy; But I told them, I knew not what Mercy to shew them; for as for my self, I had resolv'd to quit the Island with all my Men, and had taken Passage with the Captain to go for *England*: And as for the Captain, he could not carry them to *England*, other than as Prisoners in Irons to be try'd for Mutiny, and running away with the Ship; the Consequence of which, they must needs know, would be the Gallows; so that I could not tell which was best for them, unless they had a Mind to take their Fate in the Island; if they desir'd that, I did not care, as I had Liberty to leave it, I had some Inclination to give them their Lives, if they thought they could shift on Shore.

They seem'd very thankful for it, said they would much rather venture to stay there, than to be carry'd to *England* to be hang'd; so I left it on that Issue.

However, the Captain seem'd to make some Difficulty of it, as if he durst not leave them there: Upon this I seem'd a little angry with the Captain, and told him, That they were my Prisoners, not his; and that seeing I had offered them so much Favour, I would be as good as my Word; and that if he did not think fit to consent to it, I would set them at Liberty, as I found them; and if he did not like it, he might take them again if he could catch them.

Upon this they appear'd very thankful, and I accordingly set them at Liberty, and bad them retire into the Woods to the Place whence they came, and I would leave them some Fire Arms, some Ammunition, and some Directions how they should live very well, if they thought fit.

Upon this I prepar'd to go on Board the Ship, but told the Captain, that I would stay that Night to prepare my things, and desir'd him to go on Board in the mean time, and keep all right in the Ship, and send the Boat on Shore the next Day for me; ordering him in the mean time to cause the new Captain who was kill'd, to be hang'd at the Yard-Arm that these Men might see him.

When the Captain was gone, I sent for the Men up to me to my Apartment, and entred seriously into Discourse with them of their Circumstances; I told them, I thought they had made a right Choice; that if the Captain carry'd them away, they would certainly be hang'd. I shewed them the new Captain, hanging at the Yard-Arm of the Ship, and told them they had nothing less to expect.

When they had all declar'd their Willingness to stay, I then told them, I would let them into the Story of my living there, and put them into the Way of making it easy to them: Accordingly I gave them the whole History of the Place, and of my coming to it; shew'd them my Fortifications, the Way I made my Bread, planted my Corn, cured my Grapes; and in a Word, all that was necessary to make them easy: I told them the Story also of the sixteen *Spaniards* that were to be expected; for whom I left a Letter, and made them promise to treat them in common with themselves.

I left them my Fire Arms, *viz.* Five Muskets, three Fowling Pieces, and three Swords. I had above a Barrel and half of Powder left; for after the first Year or two, I used but little, and wasted none. I gave them a Description of the Way I manag'd the Goats, and Directions to milk and fatten them, and to make both Butter and Cheese.

In a Word, I gave them every Part of my own Story; and I told them, I would prevail with the Captain to leave them two Barrels of Gun-Powder more, and some Garden-Seeds, which I told them I would have been very glad of; also I gave them the Bag of Pease which the Captain had brought me to eat, and bad them be sure to sow and encrease them.

Having done all this, I left them the next Day, and went on Board the Ship: We prepared immediately to sail, but did not weigh that Night: The next Morning early, two of the five Men came swimming to the Ship's Side, and making a most lamentable Complaint of the other three, begged to be taken into the Ship, for God's Sake, for they should be murthered, and begg'd the Captain to take them on Board, tho' he hang'd them immediately.

Upon this the Captain pretended to have no Power without me; But after some Difficulty, and after their solemn Promises of Amendment, they were taken on Board, and were some time after soundly whipp'd and pickl'd; after which, they prov'd very honest and quiet Fellows.

Some time after this, the Boat was order'd on Shore, the Tide being up, with the things promised to the Men, to which the Captain at my Intercession caused their Chests and Cloaths to be added, which they took, and were very thankful for; I also encourag'd them, by telling them, that if it lay in my Way to send any Vessel to take them in, I would not forget them.

When I took leave of this Island, I carry'd on board for Reliques, the great Goat's-Skin-Cap I had made, my Umbrella, and my Parrot; also I forgot not to take the Money I formerly mention'd, which had lain by me so long useless, that it was grown rusty, or tarnish'd, and could hardly pass for Silver, till it had been a little rubb'd, and handled; as also the Money I found in the Wreck of the *Spanish* Ship.

And thus I left the Island, the Nineteenth of *December*

as I found by the Ship's Account, in the Year 1686, after I had been upon it eight and twenty Years, two Months, and 19 Days; being deliver'd from this second Captivity, the same Day of the Month, that I first made my Escape in the *Barco-Longo*, from among the *Moors* of *Sallee*.

In this Vessel, after a long Voyage, I arriv'd in *England*, the Eleventh of *June*, in the Year 1687, having been thirty and five Years absent.

When I came to *England*, I was as perfect a Stranger to all the World, as if I had never been known there. My Benefactor and faithful Steward, who I had left in Trust with my Money, was alive; but had had great Misfortunes in the World; was become a Widow the second Time, and very low in the World: I made her easy as to what she ow'd me, assuring her, I would give her no Trouble; but on the contrary, in Gratitude to her former Care and Faithfulness to me, I reliev'd her as my little Stock would afford, which at that Time would indeed allow me to do but little for her; but I assur'd her, I would never forget her former Kindness to me; nor did I forget her, when I had sufficient to help her, as shall be observ'd in its Place.

I went down afterwards into *Yorkshire*; but my Father was dead, and my Mother, and all the Family extinct, except that I found two Sisters, and two of the Children of one of my Brothers; and as I had been long ago given over for dead, there had been no Provision made for me; so that in a Word, I found nothing to relieve, or assist me; and that little Money I had, would not do much for me, as to settling in the World.

I met with one Piece of Gratitude indeed, which I did not expect; and this was, That the Master of the Ship, who I had so happily deliver'd, and by the same Means sav'd the Ship and Cargo, having given a very handsome Account to the Owners, of the Manner how I had sav'd the Lives of the Men, and the Ship, they invited me to meet them, and some other Merchants concern'd, and altogether made me a very handsome Compliment upon the Subject, and a Present of almost two hundred Pounds Sterling.

But after making several Reflections upon the Circumstances of my Life, and how little way this would go towards settling me in the World, I resolv'd to go to *Lisbon*, and see if I might not come by some Information of the State of my Plantation in the *Brasils*, and of what was become of my Partner, who I had reason to suppose had some Years now given me over for dead.

With this View I took Shipping for *Lisbon*, where I arriv'd in *April* following; my Man *Friday* accompanying me very honestly in all these Ramblings, and proving a most faithful Servant upon all Occasions.

When I came to *Lisbon*, I found out by Enquiry, and to my particular Satisfaction, my old Friend the Captain of the Ship, who first took me up at Sea, off of the Shore of *Africk:* He was now grown old, and had left off the Sea, having put his Son, who was far from a young Man, into his Ship; and who still used the *Brasil* Trade. The old Man did not know me, and indeed, I hardly knew him; but I soon brought him to my Remembrance, and as soon brought my self to his Remembrance, when I told him who I was.

After some passionate Expressions of the old Acquaintance, I enquir'd, you may be sure, after my Plantation and my Partner: The old Man told me he had not been in the *Brasils* for about nine Years; but that he could assure me, that when he came away, my Partner was living, but the Trustees, who I had join'd with him to take Cognizance of my Part, were both dead; that however, he believ'd that I would have a very good Account of the Improvement of the Plantation; for that upon the general Belief of my being cast away, and drown'd, my Trustees had given in the Account of the Produce of my Part of the Plantation, to the Procurator Fiscal, who had appropriated it, in Case I never came to claim it; one Third to the King, and two Thirds to the Monastery of St. *Augustine*, to be expended for the Benefit of the Poor, and for the Conversion of the *Indians* to the Catholick Faith; but that if I appear'd, or any one for me, to claim the Inheritance, it should be restor'd; only that the Improvement, or Annual Production, being distributed to charitable Uses, could not be restor'd; but he assur'd me, that the Steward of the King's Revenue (from Lands) and the Proviedore, or Steward of the Monastery, had taken great Care all along, that the Incumbent, that is to say my Partner, gave every Year a faithful Account of the Produce, of which they receiv'd duly my Moiety.

I ask'd him if he knew to what height of Improvement he had brought the Plantation? And, Whether he thought it might be worth looking after? Or, Whether on my going thither, I should meet with no Obstruction to my Possessing my just Right in the Moiety?

He told me, he could not tell exactly, to what Degree the Plantation was improv'd; but this he knew, that my Partner was grown exceeding Rich upon the enjoying but one half of it; and that to the best of his Remembrance, he had heard, that the King's Third of my Part, which was it seems granted away to some other Monastery, or Religious House, amounted to above two hundred Moidores a Year; that as to my being restor'd to a quiet Possession of it, there was no question to be made of that, my Partner being alive to witness my Title, and my Name being also enrolled in the Register of the Country; also he told me, That the Survivors of my two Trustees, were very fair honest People, and very Wealthy; and he believ'd I would not only have their Assistance for putting me in Possession, but would find a very considerable Sum of Money in their Hands, for my Account; being the Produce of the Farm while their Fathers held the Trust, and before it was given up as above, which as he remember'd, was for about twelve Years.

I shew'd my self a little concern'd, and uneasy at this Account, and enquir'd of the old Captain, How it came to pass, that the Trustees should thus dispose my Effects, when he knew that I had made my Will, and had made him, the *Portuguese* Captain, my universal Heir, *&c.*

He told me, that was true; but that as there was no Proof of my being dead, he could not act as Executor, until some certain Account should come of my Death, and that besides, he was not willing to intermeddle with a thing so remote; that it was true he had registred my Will, and put in his Claim; and could he have given any Account of my being dead or alive, he would have acted by Procuration, and taken Possession of the *Ingenio*, so they call'd the Sugar-House, and had given his Son, who was now at the *Brasils*, Order to do it.

But, says the old Man, I have one Piece of News to tell you, which perhaps may not be so acceptable to you as the rest, and that is, That believing you were lost, and all the World believing so also, your Partner and Trustees did offer to accompt to me in your Name, for six or eight of the first Years of Profits, which I receiv'd; but there being at that time, says he, great Disbursements for encreasing the Works, building an *Ingenio*, and buying Slaves, it did not amount to near so much as afterwards it produced: However, says the old Man, I shall give you a true Account of what I have received in all, and how I have disposed of it.

After a few Days farther Conference with this ancient Friend, he brought me an Account of the six first Years Income of my Plantation, sign'd by my Partner and the Merchants Trustees, being always deliver'd in Goods, *viz.* Tobacco in Roll, and Sugar in Chests, besides Rum, Molossus, *&c.* which is the Consequence of a Sugar Work; and I found by this Account, that every Year the Income considerably encreased; but as above, the Disbursement being large, the Sum at first was small: However, the old Man let me see, that he was Debtor to me 470 Moidores of Gold, besides 60 Chests of Sugar, and 15 double Rolls of Tobacco which were lost in his Ship; he having been Ship-wreck'd coming Home to *Lisbon* about 11 Years after my leaving the Place.

The good Man then began to complain of his Misfortunes, and how he had been obliged to make Use of my Money to recover his Losses, and buy him a Share in a new Ship: However, my old Friend, says he, you shall not want a Supply in your Necessity; and as soon as my Son returns, you shall be fully satisfy'd.

Upon this, he pulls out an old Pouch, and gives me 160 *Portugal* Moidores in Gold; and giving me the Writing of his Title to the Ship, which his Son was gone to the *Brasils* in, of which he was a Quarter Part Owner, and his Son another, he puts them both into my Hands for Security of the rest.

I was too much mov'd with the Honesty and Kindness of the poor Man, to be able to bear this; and remembring what he had done for me, how he had taken me up at Sea, and how generously he had used me on all Occasions, and particularly, how sincere a Friend he was now to me, I could hardly refrain Weeping at what he said to me: Therefore, first I asked him, if his Circumstances admitted him to spare so much Money at that time, and if it would not straiten him? He told me, he could not say but it might straiten him a little; but however it was my Money, and I might want it more than he.

Every thing the good Man said was full of Affection, and I could hardly refrain from Tears while he spoke: In short, I took 100 of the Moidores, and call'd for a Pen and Ink to give him a Receipt for them; then I returned him the rest, and told him, If ever I had Possession of the Plantation, I would return the other to him also, as indeed I afterwards did; and that as to the Bill of Sale of his Part in his Son's Ship, I would not take it by any Means; but that if I wanted the Money, I found he was honest enough to pay me; and if I did not, but came to receive what he gave me reason to expect, I would never have a Penny more from him.

When this was pass'd, the old Man began to ask me, If he should put me into a Method to make my Claim to my Plantation? I told him, I thought to go over to it my self: He said, I might do so if I pleas'd; but that if I did not, there were Ways enough to secure my Right, and immediately to appropriate the Profits to my Use; and as there were Ships in the River of *Lisbon*, just ready to go away to *Brasil*, he made me enter my Name in a Publick Register, with his Affidavit, affirming upon Oath that I was alive, and that I was the same Person who took up the Land for the Planting the said Plantation at first.

This being regularly attested by a Notary, and a Procuration affix'd, he directed me to send it with a Letter of his Writing, to a Merchant of his Acquaintance at the Place, and then propos'd my staying with him till an Account came of the Return.

Never any Thing was more honourable, than the Proceedings upon this Procuration; for in less than seven Months, I receiv'd a large Packet from the Survivors of my Trustees the Merchants, for whose Account I went to Sea, in which were the following particular Letters and Papers enclos'd.

First, There was the Account Current of the Produce of my Farm, or Plantation, from the Year when their Fathers had ballanc'd with my old *Portugal* Captain, being for six Years; the Ballance appear'd to be 1174 Moidores in my Favour.

Secondly, There was the Account of four Years more while they kept the Effects in their Hands, before the Government claim'd the Administration, as being the Effects of a Person not to be found, which they call'd *Civil Death*; and the Ballance of this, the Value of the Plantation encreasing, amounted to   Cruisadoes, which made 3241 Moidores.

Thirdly, There was the Prior of the *Augustin*'s Account, who had receiv'd the Profits for above fourteen Years; but not being to account for what was dispos'd to the Hospital, very honestly declar'd he had 872 Moidores not distributed, which he acknowledged to my Account; as to the King's Part, that refunded nothing.

There was a Letter of my Partner's, congratulating me very affectionately upon my being alive, giving me an Account how the Estate was improv'd, and what it produced a Year, with a Particular of the Number of Squares or Acres that it contained; how planted, how many Slaves there were upon it; and making two and twenty Crosses for Blessings, told me he had said so many *Ave Marias* to thank the Blessed Virgin that I was alive; inviting me very passionately to come over and take Possession of my own; and in the mean time to give him Orders to whom he should deliver my Effects, if I did not come my self; concluding with a hearty Tender of his Friendship, and that of his Family, and sent me, as a Present, seven fine Leopard's Skins, which he had it seems received from *Africa*, by some other Ship which he had sent thither, and who it seems had made a better Voyage than I: He sent me also five Chests of excellent Sweet-meats, and an hundred Pieces of Gold uncoin'd, not quite so large as Moidores.

By the same Fleet, my two Merchant Trustees ship-p'd me 1200 Chests of Sugar, 800 Rolls of Tobacco, and the rest of the whole Accompt in Gold.

I might well say, now indeed, That the latter End of *Job* was better than the Beginning. It is impossible to express here the Flutterings of my very Heart, when I look'd over these Letters, and especially when I found all my Wealth about me; for as the *Brasil* Ships come all in Fleets, the same Ships which brought my Letters, brought my Goods; and the Effects were safe in the River before the Letters came to my Hand. In a Word, I turned pale, and grew sick; and had not the old Man run and fetch'd me a Cordial, I believe the sudden Surprize of Joy had overset Nature, and I had dy'd upon the Spot.

Nay after that, I continu'd very ill, and was so some Hours, 'till a Physician being sent for, and something of the real Cause of my Illness being known, he order'd me to be let Blood; after which, I had Relief, and grew well: But I verily believe, if it had not been eas'd by a Vent given in that Manner, to the Spirits, I should have dy'd.

I was now Master, all on a Sudden, of above 5000 *l.* *Sterling* in Money, and had an Estate, as I might well call it, in the *Brasils*, of above a thousand Pounds a Year, as sure as an Estate of Lands in *England*: And in a Word, I was in a Condition which I scarce knew how to understand, or how to compose my self, for the Enjoyment of it.

The first thing I did, was to recompense my original Benefactor, my good old Captain, who had been first charitable to me in my Distress, kind to me in my Beginning, and honest to me at the End: I shew'd him all that was sent me, I told him, that next to the Providence of Heaven, which disposes all things, it was owing to him; and that it now lay on me to reward him, which I would do a hundred fold: So I first return'd to him the hundred Moidores I had receiv'd of him, then I sent for a Notary, and caused him to draw up a general Release or Discharge for the 470 Moidores, which he had acknowledg'd he ow'd me in the fullest and firmest Manner possible; after which, I caused a Procuration to be drawn, impowering him to be my Receiver of the annual Profits of my Plantation, and appointing my Partner to accompt to him, and make the Returns by the usual Fleets to him in my Name; and a Clause in the End, being a Grant of 100 Moidores a Year to him, during his Life, out of the Effects, and 50 Moidores a Year to his Son after him, for his Life: And thus I requited my old Man.

I was now to consider which Way to steer my Course next, and what to do with the Estate that Providence had thus put into my Hands; and indeed I had more Care upon my Head now, than I had in my silent State of Life in the Island, where I wanted nothing but what I had, and had nothing but what I wanted: Whereas I had now a great Charge upon me, and my Business was how to secure it. I had ne'er a Cave now to hide my Money in, or a Place where it might lye without Lock or Key, 'till it grew mouldy and tarnish'd before any Body would meddle with it: On the contrary, I knew not where to put it, or who to trust with it. My old Patron, the Captain, indeed was honest, and that was the only Refuge I had.

In the next Place, my Interest in the *Brasils* seem'd to summon me thither; but now I could not tell, how to think of going thither, 'till I had settled my Affairs, and left my Effects in some safe Hands behind me. At first I thought of my old Friend the Widow, who I knew was honest, and would be just to me; but then she was in Years, and but poor, and for ought I knew, might be in Debt; so that in a Word, I had no Way but to go back to *England* my self, and take my Effects with me.

It was some Months however before I resolved upon this; and therefore, as I had rewarded the old Captain fully, and to his Satisfaction, who had been my former Benefactor, so I began to think of my poor Widow, whose Husband had been my first Benefactor, and she, while it was in her Power, my faithful Steward and Instructor. So the first thing I did, I got a Merchant in *Lisbon* to write to his Correspondent in *London*, not only to pay a Bill, but to go find her out, and carry her in Money, an hundred Pounds from me, and to talk with her, and comfort her in her Poverty, by telling her she should, if I liv'd, have a further Supply: At the same time I sent my two Sisters in the Country, each of them an Hundred Pounds, they being, though not in Want, yet not in very good Circumstances; one having been marry'd, and left a Widow; and the other having a Husband not so kind to her as he should be.

But among all my Relations, or Acquaintances, I could not yet pitch upon one, to whom I durst commit the Gross of my Stock, that I might go away to the *Brasils*, and leave things safe behind me; and this greatly perplex'd me.

I had once a Mind to have gone to the *Brasils*, and have settled my self there; for I was, as it were, naturaliz'd to the Place; but I had some little Scruple in my Mind about Religion, which insensibly drew me back, of which I shall say more presently. However, it was not Religion that kept me from going there for the present; and as I had made no Scruple of being openly of the Religion of the Country, all the while I was among them, so neither did I yet; only that now and then having of late thought more of it, (than formerly) when I began to think of living and dying among them, I began to regret my having profess'd my self a Papist, and thought it might not be the best Religion to die with.

But, as I have said, this was not the main thing that kept me from going to the *Brasils*, but that really I did not know with whom to leave my Effects behind me; so I resolv'd at last to go to *England* with it, where, if I arrived, I concluded I should make some Acquaintance, or find some Relations that would be faithful to me; and according I prepar'd to go for *England* with all my Wealth.

In order to prepare things for my going Home, I first, the *Brasil* Fleet being just going away, resolved to give Answers suitable to the just and faithful Account of things I had from thence; and first to the Prior of St. *Augustine* I wrote a Letter full of Thanks for their just Dealings, and the Offer of the 872 Moidores, which was indisposed of, which I desir'd might be given 500 to the Monastery, and 372 to the Poor, as the Prior should direct, desiring the good *Padres* Prayers for me, and the like.

I wrote next a Letter of Thanks to my two Trustees, with all the Acknowledgment that so much Justice and Honesty call'd for; as for sending them any Present, they were far above having any Occasion of it.

Lastly, I wrote to my Partner, acknowledging his Industry in the Improving the Plantation, and his Integrity in encreasing the Stock of the Works, giving him Instructions for his future Government of my Part, according to the Powers I had left with my old Patron, to whom I desir'd him to send whatever became due to me, 'till he should hear from me more particularly; assuring him that it was my Intention, not only to come to him, but to settle my self there for the Remainder of my Life: To this I added a very handsom Present of some *Italian* Silks for his Wife, and two Daughters, for such the Captain's Son inform'd me he had; with two Pieces of fine *English* broad Cloath, the best I could get in *Lisbon*, five Pieces of black Bays, and some *Flanders* Lace of a good Value.

Having thus settled my Affairs, sold my Cargoe, and turn'd all my Effects into good Bills of Exchange, my next Difficulty was, which Way to go to *England*: I had been accustomed enough to the Sea, and yet I had a strange Aversion to going to *England* by Sea at that time; and though I could give no Reason for it, yet the Difficulty encreas'd upon me so much, that though I had once shipp'd my Baggage, in order to go, yet I alter'd my Mind, and that not once, but two or three times.

It is true, I had been very unfortunate by Sea, and this might be some of the Reason: But let no Man slight the strong Impulses of his own Thoughts in Cases of such Moment: Two of the Ships which I had singl'd out to go in, I mean, more particularly singl'd out than any other, that is to say, so as in one of them to put my things on Board, and in the other to have agreed with the Captain; I say, two of these Ships miscarry'd, *viz.* One was taken by the *Algerines*, and the other was caſt away on the *Start* near *Torbay*, and all the People drown'd except three; so that in either of those Vessels I had been made miserable; and in which moſt, it was hard to say.

Having been thus harass'd in my Thoughts, my old Pilot, to whom I communicated every thing, press'd me earneſtly not to go by Sea, but either to go by Land to the *Groyne*, and cross over the Bay of *Biscay* to *Rochell*, from whence it was but an easy and safe Journey by Land to *Paris*, and so to *Calais* and *Dover*; or to go up to *Madrid*, and so all the Way by Land thro' *France*.

In a Word, I was so prepossess'd againſt my going by Sea at all, except from *Calais* to *Dover*, that I resolv'd to travel all the Way by Land; which as I was not in Haſte, and did not value the Charge, was by much the pleasanter Way; and to make it more so, my old Captain brought an *English* Gentleman, the Son of a Merchant in *Lisbon*, who was willing to travel with me: After which, we pick'd up two more *English* Merchants also, and two young *Portuguese* Gentlemen, the laſt going to *Paris* only; so that we were in all six of us, and five Servants; the two Merchants and the two *Portuguese*, contenting themselves with one Servant, between two, to save the Charge; and as for me, I got an *English* Sailor to travel with me as a Servant, besides my Man *Friday*, who was too much a Stranger to be capable of supplying the Place of a Servant on the Road.

In this Manner I set out from *Lisbon*; and our Company being all very well mounted and armed, we made a little Troop, whereof they did me the Honour to call me

Captain, as well because I was the oldeſt Man, as because I had two Servants, and indeed was the Original of the whole Journey.

As I have troubled you with none of my Sea-Journals, so I shall trouble you now with none of my Land-Journal: But some Adventures that happen'd to us in this tedious and difficult Journey, I muſt not omit.

When we came to *Madrid*, we being all of us Strangers to *Spain*, were willing to ſtay some time to see the Court of *Spain*, and to see what was worth observing; but it being the latter Part of the Summer, we haſten'd away, and set out from *Madrid* about the Middle of *October*: But when we came to the Edge of *Navarre*, we were alarm'd at several Towns on the Way, with an Account, that so much Snow was fallen on the *French* Side of the Mountains, that several Travellers were obliged to come back to *Pampeluna*, after having attempted, at an extream Hazard, to pass on.

When we came to *Pampeluna* it self, we found it so indeed; and to me that had been always used to a hot Climate, and indeed to Countries where we could scarce bear any Cloaths on, the Cold was insufferable; nor indeed was it more painful than it was surprising, to come but ten Days before out of the old Caſtile where the Weather was not only warm but very hot, and immediately to feel a Wind from the *Pyrenean* Mountains, so very keen, so severely cold, as to be intollerable, and to endanger benumbing and perishing of our Fingers and Toes.

Poor *Friday* was really frighted when he saw the Mountains all cover'd with Snow, and felt cold Weather, which he had never seen or felt before in his Life.

To mend the Matter, when we came to *Pampeluna*, it continued snowing with so much Violence, and so long, that the People said, Winter was come before its time, and the Roads which were difficult before, were now quite impassable: For in a Word, the Snow lay in some Places too thick for us to travel; and being not hard frozen, as is the Case in Northern Countries: There was no going without being in Danger of being bury'd alive every Step. We stay'd no less than twenty Days at *Pampeluna*; when (seeing the Winter coming on, and no Likelihood of its being better; for it was the severest Winter all over *Europe* that had been known in the Memory of Man) I propos'd that we should all go away to *Fonterabia*, and there take Shipping for *Bourdeaux*, which was a very little Voyage.

But while we were considering this, there came in four *French* Gentlemen, who having been stopp'd on the *French* Side of the Passes, as we were on the *Spanish*, had found out a Guide, who traversing the Country near the Head of *Languedoc*, had brought them over the Mountains by such Ways, that they were not much incommoded with the Snow; and where they met with Snow in any Quantity, they said it was frozen hard enough to bear them and their Horses.

We sent for this Guide, who told us, he would undertake to carry us the same Way with no Hazard from the Snow, provided we were armed sufficiently to protect our selves from wild Beasts; for he said, upon these great Snows, it was frequent for some Wolves to show themselves at the Foot of the Mountains, being made ravenous for Want of Food, the Ground being covered with Snow: We told him, we were well enough prepar'd for such Creatures as they were, if he would ensure us from a Kind of two-legged Wolves, which we were told, we were in most Danger from, especially on the *French* Side of the Mountains.

He satisfy'd us there was no Danger of that kind in the Way that we were to go; so we readily agreed to follow him, as did also twelve other Gentlemen, with their Servants, some *French*, some *Spanish*; who, as I said, had attempted to go, and were oblig'd to come back again.

Accordingly, we all set out from *Pampeluna*, with our Guide, on the fifteenth of *November*; and indeed, I was surpriz'd, when instead of going forward, he came directly back with us, on the same Road that we came from *Madrid*, above twenty Miles; when being pass'd two Rivers, and come into the plain Country, we found our selves in a warm Climate again, where the Country was pleasant, and no Snow to be seen; but on a sudden, turning to his left, he approach'd the Mountains another Way; and though it is true, the Hills and Precipices look'd dreadful, yet he made so many Tours, such Meanders, and led us by such winding Ways, that we were insensibly pass'd the Height of the Mountains, without being much incumber'd with the Snow; and all on a sudden, he shew'd us the pleasant fruitful Provinces of *Languedoc* and *Gascoign*, all green and flourishing; tho' indeed it was at a great Distance, and we had some rough Way to pass yet.

We were a little uneasy however, when we found it snow'd one whole Day, and a Night, so fast, that we could not travel; but he bid us be easy, we should soon be past it all: We found indeed, that we began to descend every Day, and to come more *North* than before; and so depending upon our Guide, we went on.

It was about two Hours before Night, when our Guide being something before us, and not just in Sight, out rushed three monstrous Wolves, and after them a Bear, out of a hollow Way, adjoyning to a thick Wood; two of the

Wolves flew upon the Guide, and had he been half a Mile before us, he had been devour'd indeed, before we could have help'd him: One of them fastned upon his Horse, and the other attack'd the Man with that Violence, that he had not Time, or not Presence of Mind enough to draw his Pistol, but hollow'd and cry'd out to us most lustily; my Man *Friday* being next me, I bid him ride up, and see what was the Matter; as soon as *Friday* came in Sight of the Man, he hollow'd as loud as t'other, *O Master! O Master!* But like a bold Fellow, rode directly up to the poor Man, and with his Pistol shot the Wolf that attack'd him into the Head.

It was happy for the poor Man, that it was my Man *Friday*; for he having been us'd to that kind of Creature in his Country, had no Fear upon him; but went close up to him, and shot him as above; whereas any of us, would have fir'd at a farther Distance, and have perhaps either miss'd the Wolf, or endanger'd shooting the Man.

But it was enough to have terrify'd a bolder Man than I, and indeed it alarm'd all our Company, when with the Noise of *Friday*'s Pistol, we heard on both Sides the dismallest Howling of Wolves, and the Noise redoubled by the Eccho of the Mountains, that it was to us as if there had been a prodigious Multitude of them; and perhaps indeed there was not such a Few, as that we had no cause of Apprehensions.

However, as *Friday* had kill'd this Wolf, the other that had fastned upon the Horse, left him immediately, and fled; having happily fastned upon his Head, where the Bosses of the Bridle had stuck in his Teeth; so that he had not done him much Hurt: The Man indeed was most Hurt; for the raging Creature had bit him twice, once on the Arm, and the other Time a little above his Knee; and he was just as it were tumbling down by the Disorder of his Horse, when *Friday* came up and shot the Wolf.

It is easy to suppose, that at the Noise of *Friday*'s Pistol, we all mended our Pace, and rid up as fast as the Way (which was very difficult) would give us leave, to see what was the Matter; as soon as we came clear of the Trees, which blinded us before, we saw clearly what had been the Case, and how *Friday* had disengag'd the poor Guide; though we did not presently discern what kind of Creature it was he had kill'd.

But never was a Fight manag'd so hardily, and in such a surprizing Manner, as that which follow'd between *Friday* and the Bear, which gave us all (though at first we were surpriz'd and afraid for him) the greatest Diversion imaginable. As the Bear is a heavy, clumsey Creature, and does not gallop as the Wolf does, who is swift, and light; so he has two particular Qualities, which generally are the Rule of his Actions; First, As to Men, who are not his proper Prey; I say, not his proper Prey; because tho' I cannot say what excessive Hunger might do, which was now their Case, the Ground being all cover'd with Snow; but as to Men, he does not usually attempt them, unless they first attack him: On the contrary, if you meet him in the Woods, if you don't meddle with him, he won't meddle with you; but then you must take Care to be very Civil to him, and give him the Road; for he is a very nice Gentleman, he won't go a Step out of his Way for a Prince; nay, if you are really afraid, your best way is to look another Way, and keep going on; for sometimes if you stop, and stand still, and look steadily at him, he takes it for an Affront; but if you throw or toss any Thing at him, and it hits him, though it were but a bit of a Stick, as big as your Finger, he takes it for an Affront, and sets all his other Business aside to pursue his Revenge; for he will have Satisfaction in Point of Honour; that is his first Quality: The next is, That if he be once affronted, he will never leave you, Night or Day, till he has his Revenge; but follows at a good round rate, till he overtakes you.

My Man *Friday* had deliver'd our Guide, and when we came up to him, he was helping him off from his Horse; for the Man was both hurt and frighted, and indeed, the last more than the first; when on the sudden, we spy'd the Bear come out of the Wood, and a vast monstrous One it was, the biggest by far that ever I saw: We were all a little surpriz'd, when we saw him; but when *Friday* saw him, it was easy to see Joy and Courage in the Fellow's Countenance; *O! O! O!* Says *Friday*, three Times, pointing to him; *O* Master! *You give me te Leave! Me shakee te Hand with him*: *Me make you good laugh.*

I was surpriz'd to see the Fellow so pleas'd; *You Fool you*, says I, *he will eat you up*: *Eatee me up! Eatee me up!* Says *Friday*, twice over again; *Me eatee him up*: *Me make you good laugh*: *You all stay here*, *me show you good laugh*; so down he sits, and gets his Boots off in a Moment, and put on a Pair of Pumps (as we call the flat Shoes they wear) and which he had in his Pocket, gives my other Servant his Horse, and with his Gun away he flew swift like the Wind.

The Bear was walking softly on, and offer'd to meddle with no Body, till *Friday* coming pretty near, calls to him, as if the Bear could understand him; *Hark ye*, *hark ye*, says *Friday*, *me speakee wit you:* We follow'd at a Distance; for now being come down on the *Gascoign* side of the Mountains, we were entred a vast great Forest, where the Country was plain, and pretty open, though many Trees in it scatter'd here and there.

Friday, who had as we say, the Heels of the Bear, came up with him quickly, and takes up a great Stone, and throws at him, and hit him juſt on the Head; but did him no more harm, than if he had thrown it againſt a Wall; but it answer'd *Friday*'s End; for the Rogue was so void of Fear, that he did it purely to make the Bear follow him, and show us some Laugh as he call'd it.

As soon as the Bear felt the Stone, and saw him, he turns about, and comes after him, taking Devilish long Strides, and shuffling along at a ſtrange Rate, so as would have put a Horse to a middling Gallop; away runs *Friday*, and takes his Course, as if he run towards us for Help; so we all resolv'd to fire at once upon the Bear, and deliver my Man; though I was angry at him heartily, for bringing the Bear back upon us, when he was going about his own Business another Way; and especially I was angry that he had turn'd the Bear upon us, and then run away; and I call'd out, *You Dog*, said I, *is this your making us laugh? Come away, and take your Horse, that we may shoot the Creature*; he hears me, and crys out, *No shoot, no shoot, ſtand ſtill, you get much Laugh*. And as the nimble Creature run two Foot for the Beaſt's one, he turn'd on a sudden, on one side of us, and seeing a great Oak-Tree, fit for his Purpose, he beckon'd to us to follow, and doubling his Pace, he gets nimbly up the Tree, laying his Gun down upon the Ground, at about five or six Yards from the Bottom of the Tree.

The Bear soon came to the Tree, and we follow'd at a Diſtance; the firſt Thing he did, he ſtopp'd at the Gun, smelt to it, but let it lye, and up he scrambles into the Tree, climbing like a Cat, though so monſtrously heavy: I was amaz'd at the Folly, as I thought it, of my Man, and could not for my Life see any Thing to Laugh at yet, till seeing the Bear get up the Tree, we all rode nearer to him.

When we came to the Tree, there was *Friday* got out to the small End of a large Limb of the Tree, and the Bear got about half way to him; as soon as the Bear got out to that part where the Limb of the Tree was weaker, *Ha*, says he to us, *now you see me teachee the Bear dance*; so he falls a jumping and shaking the Bough, at which the Bear began to totter, but ſtood ſtill, and begun to look behind him, to see how he should get back; then indeed we did laugh heartily: But *Friday* had not done with him by a great deal; when he sees him ſtand ſtill, he calls out to him again, as if he had suppos'd the Bear could speak *English*; *What you no come farther*, *pray you come farther*; so he left jumping and shaking the Bough; and the Bear, juſt as if he had underſtood what he said, did come a little further, then he fell a jumping again, and the Bear ſtopp'd again.

We thought now was a good time to knock him on the Head, and I call'd to *Friday* to ſtand ſtill, and we would shoot the Bear; but he cry'd out earneſtly, *O pray! O pray! No shoot*, *me shoot*, *by and then*; he would have said, *By and by*: However, to shorten the Story, *Friday* danc'd so much, and the Bear ſtood so ticklish, that we had laughing enough indeed, but ſtill could not imagine what the Fellow would do; for firſt we thought he depended upon shaking the Bear off; and we found the Bear was too cunning for that too; for he would not go out far enough to be thrown down, but clings faſt with his great broad Claws and Feet, so that we could not imagine what would be the End of it, and where the Jeſt would be at laſt.

But *Friday* put us out of doubt quickly; for seeing the Bear cling faſt to the Bough, and that he would not be perswaded to come any farther; *Well*, *well*, says *Friday*, *you no come farther, me go, me go; you no come to me, me go come to you*; and upon this, he goes out to the smalleſt End of the Bough, where it would bend with his Weight, and gently lets himself down by it, sliding down the Bough, till he came near enough to jump down on his Feet, and away he run to his Gun, takes it up, and ſtands ſtill.

Well, said I to him *Friday*, What will you do now? Why don't you shoot him? *No shoot*, says *Friday*, *no yet, me shoot now, me no kill*; *me ſtay, give you one more laugh*; and indeed so he did, as you will see presently; for when the Bear see his Enemy gone, he comes back from the Bough where he ſtood; but did it mighty leisurely, looking behind him every Step, and coming backward till he got into the Body of the Tree; then with the same hinder End foremoſt, he came down the Tree, grasping it with his Claws, and moving one Foot at a Time, very leisurely; at this Juncture, and juſt before he could set his hind Feet upon the Ground, *Friday* ſtept up close to him, clapt the Muzzle of his Piece into his Ear, and shot him dead as a Stone.

Then the Rogue turn'd about, to see if we did not laugh, and when he saw we were pleas'd by our Looks, he falls a laughing himself very loud; *so we kill Bear in my Country*, says *Friday*; so you kill them, says I, Why you have no Guns: *No*, says he, *no Gun, but shoot, great much long Arrow.*

This was indeed a good Diversion to us; but we were ſtill in a wild Place, and our Guide very much hurt, and what to do we hardly knew; the Howling of Wolves run much in my Head; and indeed, except the Noise I once heard on the Shore of *Africa*, of which I have said something already, I never heard any thing that filled me with so much Horrour.

These things, and the Approach of Night, called us off, or else, as *Friday* would have had us, we should certainly have taken the Skin of this monstrous Creature off, which was worth saving; but we had three Leagues to go, and our Guide hasten'd us, so we left him, and went forward on our Journey.

The Ground was still cover'd with Snow, tho' not so deep and dangerous as on the Mountains, and the ravenous Creatures, as we heard afterwards, were come down into the Forest and plain Country, press'd by Hunger to seek for Food; and had done a great deal of Mischief in the Villages, where they surpriz'd the Country People, kill'd a great many of their Sheep and Horses, and some People too.

We had one dangerous Place to pass, which our Guide told us, if there were any more Wolves in the Country, we should find them there; and this was in a small Plain, surrounded with Woods on every Side, and a long narrow Defile or Lane, which we were to pass to get through the Wood, and then we should come to the Village where we were to lodge.

It was within half an Hour of Sun-set when we entred the first Wood; and a little after Sun-set, when we came into the Plain. We met with nothing in the first Wood, except, that in a little Plain within the Wood, which was not above two Furlongs over, we saw five great Wolves cross the Road, full Speed one after another, as if they had been in Chase of some Prey, and had it in View, they took no Notice of us, and were gone, and out of our Sight in a few Moments.

Upon this our Guide, who by the Way was a wretched faint-hearted Fellow, bid us keep in a ready Posture; for he believed there were more Wolves a coming.

We kept our Arms ready, and our Eyes about us, but we saw no more Wolves, 'till we came thro' that Wood, which was near half a League, and entred the Plain; as soon as we came into the Plain, we had Occasion enough to look about us: The first Object we met with, was a dead Horse; that is to say, a poor Horse which the Wolves had kill'd, and at least a Dozen of them at Work; we could not say eating of him, but picking of his Bones rather; for they had eaten up all the Flesh before.

We did not think fit to disturb them at their Feast, neither did they take much Notice of us: *Friday* would have let fly at them, but I would not suffer him by any Means; for I found we were like to have more Business upon our Hands than we were aware of. We were not gone half over the Plain, but we began to hear the Wolves howl in the Wood on our Left, in a frightful Manner, and presently after we saw about a hundred coming on directly towards us, all in a Body, and most of them in a Line, as regularly as an Army drawn up by experienc'd Officers. I scarce knew in what Manner to receive them; but found to draw ourselves in a close Line was the only Way: so we form'd in a Moment: But that we might not have too much Interval, I order'd, that only every other Man should fire, and that the others who had not fir'd should stand ready to give them a second Volley immediately, if they continued to advance upon us, and that then those who had fir'd at first, should not pretend to load their Fusees again, but stand ready with every one a Pistol; for we were all arm'd with a Fusee, and a Pair of Pistols each Man; so we were by this Method able to fire six Volleys, half of us at a Time; however, at present we had no Necessity; for upon firing the first Volley, the Enemy made a full Stop, being terrify'd as well with the Noise, as with the Fire; four of them being shot into the Head, dropp'd; several others were wounded, and went bleeding off, as we could see by the Snow: I found they ſtopp'd, but did not immediately retreat; whereupon remembring that I had been told, that the fierceſt Creatures were terrify'd at the Voice of a Man, I caus'd all our Company to hollow as loud as we could; and I found the Notion not altogether miſtaken; for upon our Shout, they began to retire, and turn about; then I order'd a second Volley to be fir'd, in their Rear, which put them to the Gallop, and away they went to the Woods.

This gave us leisure to charge our Pieces again, and that we might loose no Time, we kept going; but we had but little more than loaded our Fusees, and put ourselves into a Readiness, when we heard a terrible Noise in the same Wood, on our Left, only that it was farther onward the same Way we were to go.

The Night was coming on, and the Light began to be dusky, which made it worse on our Side; but the Noise encreasing, we could easily perceive that it was the Howling and Yelling of those hellish Creatures; and on a sudden, we perceiv'd 2 or 3 Troops of Wolves, one on our Left, one behind us, and one on our Front; so that we seem'd to be surrounded with 'em; however, as they did not fall upon us, we kept our Way forward, as faſt as we could make our Horses go, which the Way being very rough, was only a good large Trot; and in this Manner we came in View of the Entrance of a Wood, through which we were to pass, at the farther side of the Plain; but we were greatly surpriz'd, when coming nearer the Lane, or Pass, we saw a confus'd Number of Wolves ſtanding juſt at the Entrance.

On a sudden, at another opening of the Wood, we

heard the Noise of a Gun; and looking that Way, out rush'd a Horse, with a Saddle, and a Bridle on him, flying like the Wind, and sixteen or seventeen Wolves after him, full Speed; indeed, the Horse had the Heels of them; but as we suppos'd that he could not hold it at that rate, we doubted not but they would get up with him at laſt, and no queſtion but they did.

But here we had a moſt horrible Sight; for riding up to the Entrance where the Horse came out, we found the Carcass of another Horse, and of two Men, devour'd by the ravenous Creatures, and one of the Men was no doubt the same who we heard fir'd the Gun; for there lay a Gun juſt by him, fir'd off; but as to the Man, his Head, and the upper Part of his Body was eaten up.

This fill'd us with Horror, and we knew not what Course to take, but the Creatures resolv'd us soon; for they gather'd about us presently, in hopes of Prey; and I verily believe there were three hundred of them: It happen'd very much to our Advantage, that at the Entrance into the Wood, but a little Way from it, there lay some large Timber Trees, which had been cut down the Summer before, and I suppose lay there for Carriage; I drew my little Troop in among those Trees, and placing our selves in a Line, behind one long Tree, I advis'd them all to light, and keeping that Tree before us, for a Breaſt Work, to ſtand in a Triangle, or three Fronts, enclosing our Horses in the Center.

We did so, and it was well we did; for never was a more furious Charge than the Creatures made upon us in the Place; they came on us with a growling kind of a Noise (and mounted the Piece of Timber, which as I said, was our Breaſt Work) as if they were only rushing upon their Prey; and this Fury of theirs, it seems, was principally occasion'd by their seeing our Horses behind us, which was the Prey they aim'd at: I order'd our Men to fire as before, every other Man; and they took their Aim so sure, that indeed they kill'd several of the Wolves at the first Volley; but there was a Necessity to keep a continual Firing; for they came on like Devils, those behind pushing on those before.

When we had fir'd our second Volley of our Fusees, we thought they stopp'd a little, and I hop'd they would have gone off; but it was but a Moment; for others came forward again; so we fir'd two Volleys of our Pistols, and I believe in these four Firings, we had kill'd seventeen or eighteen of them, and lam'd twice as many; yet they came on again.

I was loath to spend our last Shot too hastily; so I call'd my Servant, not my Man *Friday*; for he was better employ'd; for with the greatest Dexterity imaginable, he had charg'd my Fusee, and his own, while we were engag'd; but as I said, I call'd my other Man, and giving him a Horn of Powder, I bad him lay a Train, all along the Piece of Timber, and let it be a large Train; he did so, and had but just Time to get away, when the Wolves came up to it, and some were got up upon it; when I snapping an uncharg'd Pistol, close to the Powder, set it on fire; those that were upon the Timber were scorcht with it, and six or seven of them fell, or rather jump'd in among us, with the Force and Fright of the Fire; we dispatch'd these in an Instant, and the rest were so frighted with the Light, which the Night, for it was now very near Dark, made more terrible, that they drew back a little.

Upon which I order'd our last Pistol to be fir'd off in one Volley, and after that we gave a Shout; upon this, the Wolves turn'd Tail, and we sally'd immediately upon near twenty lame Ones, who we found ſtruggling on the Ground, and fell a cutting them with our Swords, which answer'd our Expectation; for the Crying and Howling they made, was better underſtood by their Fellows, so that they all fled and left us.

We had, firſt and laſt, kill'd about three Score of them; and had it been Day-Light, we had kill'd many more: The Field of Battle being thus clear'd, we made forward again; for we had ſtill near a League to go. We heard the ravenous Creatures houl and yell in the Woods as we went, several Times; and sometimes we fancy'd we saw some of them, but the Snow dazling our Eyes, we were not certain; so in about an Hour more, we came to the Town, where we were to lodge, which we found in a terrible Fright, and all in Arms; for it seems, that the Night before, the Wolves and some Bears had broke into the Village in the Night, and put them in a terrible Fright; and they were oblig'd to keep Guard Night and Day, but especially in the Night, to preserve their Cattle, and indeed their People.

The next Morning our Guide was so ill, and his Limbs swell'd with the rankling of his two Wounds, that he could go no farther; so we were oblig'd to take a new Guide there, and go to *Thoulouse*, where we found a warm Climate, a fruitful pleasant Country, and no Snow, no Wolves, or any Thing like them; but when we told our Story at *Thoulouse*, they told us it was nothing but what was ordinary in the great Foreſt at the Foot of the Mountains, especially when the Snow lay on the Ground: But they enquir'd much what kind of a Guide we had gotten, that would venture to bring us that Way in such a severe Season: and told us, it was very much we were not all devour'd. When we told them how we plac'd our selves, and the Horses in the Middle, they blam'd us exceedingly, and told us it was fifty to one but we had been all destroy'd; for it was the Sight of the Horses which made the Wolves so furious, seeing their Prey; and that at other Times they are really afraid of a Gun; but the being excessive Hungry, and raging on that Account, the Eagerness to come at the Horses had made them sensless of Danger; and that if we had not by the continu'd Fire, and at last by the Stratagem of the Train of Powder, master'd them, it had been great Odds but that we had been torn to Pieces; whereas had we been content to have sat still on Horseback, and fir'd as Horsemen, they would not have taken the Horses for so much their own, when Men were on their Backs, as otherwise; and withal they told us, that at last, if we had stood altogether, and left our Horses, they would have been so eager to have devour'd them, that we might have come off safe, especially having our Fire Arms in our Hands, and being so many in Number.

For my Part, I was never so sensible of Danger in my Life; for seeing above three hundred Devils come roaring and open mouth'd to devour us, and having nothing to shelter us, or retreat to, I gave my self over for lost; and as it was, I believe, I shall never care to cross those Mountains again; I think I would much rather go a thousand Leagues by Sea, though I were sure to meet with a Storm once a Week.

I have nothing uncommon to take Notice of, in my Passage through *France*; nothing but what other Travellers have given an Account of, with much more Advantage than I can. I travell'd from *Thoulouse* to *Paris*, and without any considerable Stay, came to *Callais*, and landed safe at *Dover*, the fourteenth of *January*, after having had a severely cold Season to travel in.

I was now come to the Center of my Travels, and had in a little Time all my new discover'd Eſtate safe about me, the Bills of Exchange which I brought with me having been very currently paid.

My principal Guide, and Privy Councellor, was my good antient Widow, who in Gratitude for the Money I had sent her, thought no Pains too much, or Care too great, to employ for me; and I truſted her so entirely with every Thing, that I was perfectly easy as to the Security of my Effects; and indeed, I was very happy from my Beginning, and now to the End, in the unspotted Integrity of this good Gentlewoman.

And now I began to think of leaving my Effects with this Woman, and setting out for *Lisbon*, and so to the *Brasils*; but now another Scruple came in my Way, and that was Religion; for as I had entertain'd some Doubts about the *Roman* Religion, even while I was abroad, especially in my State of Solitude; so I knew there was no going to the *Brasils* for me, much less going to settle there, unless I resolv'd to embrace the *Roman* Catholick Religion, without any Reserve; unless on the other hand, I resolv'd to be a Sacrifice to my Principles, be a Martyr for Religion, and die in the Inquisition; so I resolv'd to ſtay at Home, and if I could find Means for it, to dispose of my Plantation.

To this Purpose I wrote to my old Friend at *Lisbon*, who in Return gave me Notice, that he could easily dispose of it there: But that if I thought fit to give him Leave to offer it in my Name to the two Merchants, the Survivors of my Truſtees, who liv'd in the *Brasils*, who muſt fully underſtand the Value of it, who liv'd juſt upon the Spot, and who I knew were very rich; so that he believ'd they would be fond of buying it; he did not doubt, but

I should make 4 or 5000 Pieces of Eight, the more of it.

Accordingly I agreed, gave him Order to offer it to them, and he did so; and in about 8 Months more, the Ship being then return'd, he sent me Account, that they had accepted the Offer, and had remitted 33000 Pieces of Eight, to a Correspondent of theirs at *Lisbon*, to pay for it.

In Return, I sign'd the Instrument of Sale in the Form which they sent from *Lisbon*, and sent it to my old Man, who sent me Bills of Exchange for 328000 Pieces of Eight to me, for the Estate; reserving the Payment of 100 Moidores a Year to him, the old Man, during his Life, and 50 Moidores afterwards to his Son for his Life, which I had promised them, which the Plantation was to make good as a Rent-Charge. And thus I have given the first Part of a Life of Fortune and Adventure, a Life of Providences Checquer-Work, and of a Variety which the World will seldom be able to show the like of: Beginning foolishly, but closing much more happily than any Part of it ever gave me Leave so much as to hope for.

Any one would think, that in this State of complicated good Fortune, I was past running any more Hazards; and so indeed I had been, if other Circumstances had concurr'd, but I was inur'd to a wandring Life, had no Family, not many Relations, nor, however rich had I contracted much Acquaintance; and though I had sold my Estate in the *Brasils*, yet I could not keep the Country out of my Head, and had a great Mind to be upon the Wing again, especially I could not resist the strong Inclination I had to see my Island, and to know if the poor *Spaniards* were in Being there, and how the Rogues I left there had used them.

My true Friend, the Widow, earnestly diswaded me from it, and so far prevail'd with me, that for almost seven Years she prevented my running Abroad; during which time, I took my two Nephews, the Children of one of my Brothers into my Care: The eldest having something of his own, I bred up as a Gentleman, and gave him a Settlement of some Addition to his Estate, after my Decease; the other I put out to a Captain of a Ship; and after five Years, finding him a sensible bold enterprising young Fellow, I put him into a good Ship, and sent him to Sea: And this young Fellow afterwards drew me in, as old as I was, to farther Adventures my self.

In the mean time, I in Part settled my self here; for first of all I marry'd, and that not either to my Disadvantage or Dissatisfaction, and had three Children, two Sons and one Daughter: But my Wife dying, and my Nephew coming Home with good Success from a Voyage to *Spain*, my Inclination to go Abroad, and his Importunity prevailed and engag'd me to go in his Ship, as a private Trader to the *East Indies*: This was in the Year 1694.

In this Voyage I visited my new Collony in the Island, saw my Successors the *Spaniards*, had the whole Story of their Lives, and of the Villains I left there; how at first they insulted the poor *Spaniards*, how they afterwards agreed, disagreed, united, separated, and how at last the *Spaniards* were oblig'd to use Violence with them, how they were subjected to the *Spaniards*, how honestly the *Spaniards* used them; a History, if it were entred into, as full of Variety and wonderful Accidents, as my own Part, particularly also as to their Battles with the *Carribeans*, who landed several times upon the Island, and as to the Improvement they made upon the Island it self, and how five of them made an Attempt upon the main Land, and brought away eleven Men and five Women Prisoners, by which, at my coming, I found about twenty young Children on the Island.

Here I ﬅay'd about 20 Days, left them Supplies of all necessary things, and particularly of Arms, Powder, Shot, Cloaths, Tools, and two Workmen, which I brought from *England* with me, *viz.* a Carpenter and a Smith.

Besides this, I shar'd the Island into Parts with 'em, reserv'd to my self the Property of the whole, but gave them such Parts respectively as they agreed on; and having settled all things with them, and engaged them not to leave the Place, I left them there.

From thence I touch'd at the *Brasils*, from whence I sent a Bark, which I bought there, with more People to the Island, and in it, besides other Supplies, I sent seven Women, being such as I found proper for Service, or for Wives to such as would take them: As to the *English* Men, I promis'd them to send them some Women from *England*, with a good Cargoe of Necessaries, if they would apply themselves to Planting, which I afterwards perform'd. And the Fellows prov'd very honeﬅ and diligent after they were maﬅer'd, and had their Properties set apart for them. I sent them also from the *Brasils* five Cows, three of them being big with Calf, some Sheep, and some Hogs, which, when I came again, were considerably encreas'd.

But all these things, with an Account how 300 *Caribbees* came and invaded them, and ruin'd their Plantations, and how they fought with that whole Number twice, and were at firﬅ defeated, and three of them kill'd; but at laﬅ a Storm deﬅroying their Enemies Canoes, they famish'd or deﬅroy'd almoﬅ all the reﬅ, and renew'd and recover'd the Possession of their Plantation, and ſtill liv'd upon the Island.

All these things, with some very surprizing Incidents in some new Adventures of my own, for ten Years more, I may perhaps give a farther Account of hereafter.

FINIS.

The Farther Adventures of
ROBINSON CRUSOE

Being the Second and Last Part of his
LIFE, and the Strange Surprizing
ACCOUNTS of his TRAVELS
Round three Parts of the
Globe

Written by Himself

To which is added a Map of the World,
in which is Delineated the Voyages of
ROBINSON CRUSOE

THE

FARTHER ADVENTURES

OF

ROBINSON CRUSOE, &c.

THAT homely Proverb used on so many Occasions in *England*, *viz.* *That what is bred in the Bone will not go out of the Flesh*, was never more verify'd, than in the Story of my Life. Any one would think, that after thirty-five Years Affliction, and a Variety of unhappy Circumstances, which few Men, if any ever, went thro' before, and after near seven Years of Peace and Enjoyment in the Fulness of all Things; grown old, and when, *if ever*, it might be allowed me to have had Experience of every State of middle Life, and to know which was most adapted to make a Man compleatly happy: I say, after all this, any one would have thought that the native Propensity to rambling, which I gave an Account of in my first Setting out into the World, to have been so predominate in my Thoughts, should be worn out, the volatile Part be fully evacuated, or at least condens'd, and I might at 61 Years of Age have been a little enclin'd to stay at Home, and have done venturing Life and Fortune any more.

Nay farther, the common Motive of foreign Adventures was taken away in me; for I had no Fortune to make, I had nothing to seek: If I had gain'd ten thousand Pound, I had been no richer; for I had already sufficient for me, and for those I had to leave it to; and that I had was visibly encreasing; for having no great Family, I could not spend the Income of what I had, unless I would set up for an expensive Way of Living, such as a great Family, Servants, Equipage, Gayety, and *the like*, which were Things I had no Notion of, or Inclination to; so that I had nothing indeed to do, but to sit still, and fully enjoy what I had got, and see it encrease daily upon my Hands.

Yet all these Things had no Effect upon me, or at least, not enough to resist the strong Inclination I had to go Abroad again, which hung about me like a chronical Distemper; particularly the Desire of seeing my new Plantation in the Island, and the Colony I left there, run in my Head continually. I dream'd of it all Night, and my Imagination run upon it all Day; it was uppermost in all my Thoughts, and my Fancy work'd so steadily and strongly upon it, that I talk'd of it in my Sleep; in short, nothing could remove it out of my Mind; it even broke so violently into all my Discourses, that it made my Conversation tiresome; for I could talk of nothing else, all my Discourse run into it, even to Impertinence, and I saw it my self.

I have often heard Persons of good Judgment say, That all the Stir People make in the World about Ghosts and Apparitions, is owing to the Strength of Imagination, and the powerful Operation of Fancy in their Minds; that there is no such Thing as a Spirit appearing, or a Ghost walking, *and the like*: That Peoples poring affectionately upon the past Conversation of their deceas'd Friends, so realizes it to them, that they are capable of fancying upon some extraordinary Circumstances, that they see them; talk to them, and are answered by them, when, in Truth, there is nothing but Shadow and Vapour in the Thing; and they really know nothing of the Matter.

For my Part, I know not to this Hour, whether there are any such Things as real Apparitions, Spectres, or

Walking of People after they are dead, or whether there is any Thing in the Stories they tell us of that Kind, more than the Product of Vapours, sick Minds, and wandring Fancies; But this I know, that my Imagination work'd up to such a Height, and brought me into such Extasies of Vapours, or what else I may call it, that I actually suppos'd my self, often-times upon the Spot, at my old Castle behind the Trees; saw my old *Spaniard*, *Friday's* Father, and the reprobate Sailors I left upon the Island; nay, I fancy'd I talk'd with them, and look'd at them so steadily, tho' I was broad awake, as at Persons just before me; and this I did till I often frighted my self with the Images my Fancy represented to me: One Time in my Sleep I had the Villany of the 3 Pyrate Sailors so lively related to me by the first *Spaniard* and *Friday's* Father, that it was surprizing; they told me how they barbarously attempted to murder all the *Spaniards*, and that they set Fire to the Provisions they had laid up, on Purpose to distress and starve them, Things that I had never heard of, and that indeed were never all of them true in Fact: But it was so warm in my Imagination, and so realiz'd to me, that to the Hour I saw them, I could not be persuaded, but that it was or would be true; also how I resented it, when the *Spaniard* complain'd to me, and how I brought them to Justice, try'd them before me, and order'd them all three to be hang'd: What there was really in this, shall be seen in its Place: For however, I came to form such Things in my Dream, and what secret Converse of Spirits injected it, yet there was very much of it true. I say, I own, that this Dream had nothing in it literally and specifically true: But the general Part was so true, the base villainous Behaviour of these three harden'd Rogues was such, and had been so much worse than all I can describe, that the

Dream had too much Similitude of the Fact, and as I would afterwards have punished them severely; so if I had hang'd them all, I had been much in the Right, and should ha' been justifiable both by the Laws of God and Man.

But to return to my Story; in this Kind of Temper I had liv'd some Years, I had no Enjoyment of my Life, no pleasant Hours, no agreeable Diversion, but what had some Thing or other of this in it; so that my Wife, who saw my Mind so wholly bent upon it, told me very seriously one Night, That she believ'd there was some secret powerful Impulse of Providence upon me, which had determin'd me to go thither again; and that she found nothing hindred my going, but my being engag'd to a Wife and Children. She told me that it was true she could not think of parting with me; but as she was assur'd, that if she was dead, it would be the first Thing I would do: So as it seem'd to her, that the Thing was determin'd above, she would not be the only Obstruction: For if I thought fit, and resolv'd to go —— here she found me very intent upon her Words, and that I look'd very earnestly at her; so that it a little disorder'd her, and she stopp'd. I ask'd her, Why she did not go on, and say out what she was going to say? But I perceiv'd her Heart was too full, and some Tears stood in her Eyes: Speak out my Dear, said I, Are you willing I should go? No, *says she very affectionately*, I am far from willing: But if you are resolv'd to go, says she, and rather than I will be the only Hindrance, I will go with you; for tho' I think it a most preposterous Thing for one of your Years, and in your Condition, yet if it must be, said she again weeping, I won't leave you; for if it be of Heaven, you must do it. There is no resisting it; and if Heaven makes it your Duty to go, he will also make it mine to go with you, or otherwise dispose of me, that I may not obstruct it.

This affectionate Behaviour of my Wife's brought me a little out of the Vapours, and I began to consider what I was a doing; I corrected my wandring Fancy, and began to argue with my self sedately, what Business I had after threescore Years, and after such a Life of tedious Sufferings and Disasters, and closed in so happy and easy a Manner, I say, what Business I had to rush into new Hazards, and put my self upon Adventures, fit only for Youth and Poverty to run into.

With those Thoughts, I considered my new Engagement, that I had a Wife, one Child born, and my Wife then great with Child of another; that I had all the World could give me, and had no Need to seek Hazards for Gain; that I was declining in Years, and ought to think rather of leaving what I had gain'd, than of seeking to encrease it; that as to what my Wife had said, of its being an Impulse from Heaven, and that it should be my Duty to go, I had no Notion of that; so after many of these Cogitations, I struggled with the Power of my Imagination, reason'd my self out of it, *as I believe People may always do in like Cases, if they will*; and, in a Word, I conquer'd it; compos'd my self with such Arguments as occur'd to my Thought, and which my present Condition furnish'd me plentifully with, and particularly, as the most effectual Method, I resolv'd to divert my self with other Things, and to engage in some Business that might effectually tye me up from any more Excursions of this Kind; for I found that Thing return upon me chiefly when I was idle, had nothing to do, or any Thing of Moment immediately before me.

To this Purpose I bought a little Farm in the County

of *Bedford*, and resolv'd to remove my self thither. I had a little convenient House upon it, and the Land about it I found was capable of great Improvement, and that it was many Ways suited to my Inclination, which delighted in Cultivating, Managing, Planting, and Improving of Land; and particularly, being an Inland Country, I was remov'd from conversing among Ships, Sailors, and Things relating to the remote Part of the World.

In a Word, I went down to my Farm, settled my Family, bought me Ploughs, Harrows, a Cart, Wagon, Horses, Cows, Sheep; and setting seriously to Work, became in one half Year, a meer Country Gentleman; my Thoughts were entirely taken up in managing my Servants, cultivating the Ground, Enclosing, Planting, *&c.* and I liv'd, as I thought, the most agreeable Life that Nature was capable of directing, or that a Man always bred to Misfortunes was capable of being retreated to.

I farm'd upon my own Land, I had no Rent to pay, was limited by no Articles; I could pull up or cut down as I pleased: What I planted, was for my self, and what I improved, was for my Family; and having thus left off the Thoughts of Wandring, I had not the least Discomfort in any Part of Life, as to this World. Now I thought indeed, that I enjoy'd the middle State of Life, that my Father so earnestly recommended to me, and liv'd a kind of heavenly Life, something like what is described by the Poet upon the Subject of a Country Life.

Free from Vices, free from Care,
Age has no Pain, and Youth no Snare.

But in the Middle of all this Felicity, one Blow from unforeseen Providence unhing'd me at once; and not only made a Breach upon me inevitable and incurable, but drove me, by its Consequences, into a deep Relapse into the wandring Disposition, which, as I may say, being born in my very Blood, soon recover'd its hold of me, and like the Returns of a violent Distemper, came on with an irresistible Force upon me; so that nothing could make any more Impression upon me. This Blow was the Loss of my Wife.

It is not my Business here to write an Elegy upon my Wife, give a Character of her particular Virtues, and make my Court to the Sex by the Flattery of a Funeral Sermon. She was, in a few Words, the Stay of all my Affairs, the Center of all my Enterprizes, the Engine, that by her Prudence reduc'd me to that happy Compass I was in, from the most extravagant and ruinous Project that fluttered in my Head, as above; and did more to guide my rambling Genius, than a Mother's Tears, a Father's Instructions, a Friend's Counsel, or all my own reasoning Powers could do. I was happy in listening to her Tears, and in being mov'd by her Entreaties, and to the last Degree desolate and dislocated in the World by the Loss of her.

When she was gone, the World look'd aukwardly round me; I was as much a Stranger in it, in my Thoughts, as I was in the *Brasils*, when I went first on Shore there; and as much alone, except as to the Assistance of Servants, as I was in my Island. I knew neither what to do, or what not to do. I saw the World busy round me, one Part labouring for Bread, and the other Part squandring in vile Excesses or empty Pleasures, equally miserable, because the End they propos'd still fled from them; for the Man of Pleasure every Day surfeited of his Vice, and heaped up Work for Sorrow and Repentance; and the Men of Labour spent their Strength in daily Strugglings for Bread to maintain the vital Strength they labour'd with, so living in a daily Circulation of Sorrow, living but to work, and working but to live, as if daily Bread were the only End of wearisome Life, and a wearisome Life the only Occasion of daily Bread.

This put me in Mind of the Life I liv'd in my Kingdom, the Island; where I suffer'd no more Corn to grow, because I did not want it; and bred no more Goats, because I had no more Use for them: Where the Money lay in the Drawer 'till it grew mouldy, and had scarce the Favour to be look'd upon in 20 Years.

All these Things, had I improv'd them as I ought to have done, and as Reason and Religion had dictated to me, would have taught to me to search farther than human Enjoyments for a full Felicity, and that there was something which certainly was the Reason and End of Life, superiour to all these Things, and which was either to be possess'd, or at least hop'd for on this Side the Grave.

But my Sage Counsellor was gone, I was like a Ship without a Pilot, that could only run afore the Wind: My Thoughts run all away again into the old Affair, my Head quite was turn'd with the Whimsies of foreign Adventures, and all the pleasant innocent Amusements of my Farm, and my Garden, my Cattle, and my Family, which before entirely possest me, were nothing to me, had no Relish, and were like Musick to one that has no Ear, or Food to one that has no Taste: In a Word, I resolv'd to leave off House-keeping, lett my Farm, and return to *London*; and in a few Months after, I did so.

When I came to *London*, I was still as uneasy as I was before, I had no Relish to the Place, no Employment in it, nothing to do but to saunter about like an idle Person, of whom it may be said, he is perfectly useless in God's

Creation; and it is not one Farthing Matter to the rest of his Kind, whether he be dead or alive. This also was the Life which of all Circumstances of Life was the most my Aversion, who had been all my Days used to an active Life; and I would often say to my self, *A State of Idleness is the very Dregs of Life*; and indeed I thought I was much more suitably employ'd, when I was 26 Days a making me a Deal Board.

It was now the Beginning of the Year 1693, when my Nephew, who as I had observ'd before I had brought up to the Sea, and had made him Commander of a Ship, was come Home from a short Voyage to *Bilboa*, being the first he had made; and he came to me, and told me, that some Merchants of his Acquaintance had been proposing to him to go a Voyage for them to the *East Indies* and to *China*, as private Traders: And now Uncle, says he, if you will go to Sea with me, I'll engage to land you upon your old Habitation in the Island, for we are to touch at the *Brasils*.

Nothing can be a greater Demonstration of a future State, and of the Existence of an invisible World, than the Concurrence of second Causes, with the Ideas of Things, which we form in our Minds, perfectly reserv'd, and not communicated to any in the World.

My Nephew knew nothing how far my Distemper of wandring was return'd upon me, and I knew nothing of what he had in his Thoughts to say, when that very Morning before he came to me, I had in a great deal of Confusion of Thought, and revolving every Part of my Circumstances in my Mind, come to this Resolution, *viz*. That I would go to *Lisbon*, and consult with my old Sea-Captain, and so if it was rational and practicable, I would go and see the Island again, and see what was become of my People there. I had pleas'd my self with the Thoughts of peopling the Place, and carrying Inhabitants from hence, getting a Patent for the Possession, and I know not what; when in the Middle of all this, in comes my Nephew, as I have said, with his Project of carrying me thither, in his Way to the *East Indies*.

I paus'd a while at his Words, and looking steadily at him, *What Devil*, said I, *sent you of this unlucky Errand?* My Nephew star'd as if he had been frighted at first; but perceiving I was not much displeas'd with the Proposal, he recover'd himself. I hope it may not be an unlucky Proposal, Sir, says he, I dare say you would be pleas'd to see your new Colony there, where you once reigned with more Felicity, than most of your Brother Monarchs in the World.

In a Word, the Scheme hit so exactly with my Temper, that is to say, the Prepossession I was under, and of which I have said so much, that I told him in few Words, if he agreed with the Merchants, I would go with him: But I told him, I would not promise to go any farther than my own Island. Why Sir, says he, you don't want to be left there again, I hope? Why, said I, can you not take me up again in your Return? He told me, it could not be possible, that the Merchants would allow him to come that Way with a loaden Ship of such value, it being a Month's Sail out of his Way, and might be three or four: Besides, Sir, if I should miscarry, said he, and not return at all, then you would be just reduced to the Condition you were in before.

This was very rational; but we both found out a Remedy for it, which was to carry a framed Sloop on board the Ship, which being taken in Pieces, and shipp'd on board the Ship, might by the Help of some Carpenters, who we agreed to carry with us, be set up again in the Island, and finish'd, fit to go to Sea in a few Days.

I was not long resolving; for indeed the Importunities of my Nephew join'd in so effectually with my Inclination, that nothing could oppose me: On the other Hand, my Wife being dead, I had no Body concern'd themselves so much for me, as to perswade me one Way or other, except my ancient good Friend the Widow, who earnestly struggled with me to consider my Years, my easy Circumstances, and the needless Hazards of a long Voyage; and above all, my young Children: But it was all to no Purpose, I had an irresistible Desire to the Voyage; and I told her, I thought there was something so uncommon in the Impressions I had upon my Mind for the Voyage, that it would be a kind of resisting Providence, if I should attempt to stay at Home; after which, she ceas'd her Expostulations, and join'd with me, not only in making Provision for my Voyage, but also in settling my Family Affairs for my Absence, and providing for the Education of my Children.

In Order to this, I made my Will, and settled the Estate I had, in such a Manner for my Children, and placed in such Hands, that I was perfectly easy and satisfy'd they would have Justice done them, whatever might befal me; and for their Education, I left it wholly to my Widow, with a sufficient Maintenance to her self for her Care: All which she richly deserv'd; for no Mother could have taken more Care in their Education, or understand it better; and as she liv'd 'till I came Home, I also liv'd to thank her for it.

My Nephew was ready to sail about the Beginning of *January* 1694-5, and I with my Man *Friday* went on board in the *Downs* the 8th, having besides that Sloop which I mention'd above, a very considerable Cargo of all Kinds of necessary Things for my Colony, which if I did not find in good Condition, I resolv'd to leave so.

First, I carry'd with me some Servants, who I purpos'd to place there, as Inhabitants, or at least to set on Work there upon my own Account while I stay'd, and either to leave them there, or carry them forward as they should appear willing; particularly, I carry'd two Carpenters, a Smith, and a very handy ingenious Fellow, who was a Cooper by Trade but was also a general Mechanick; for he was dextrous at making Wheels, and Hand-Mills to grind Corn, was a good Turner, and a good Pot-Maker; he also made any Thing that was proper to make of Earth, or of Wood; in a Word, we call'd him *Our Jack of all Trades.*

With these I carry'd a Taylor, who had offer'd himself to go Passenger to the *East Indies* with my Nephew, but afterwards consented to stay on our New Plantation, and prov'd a most necessary handy Fellow, as could be desir'd, in many other Businesses, besides that of this Trade; for as I observ'd formerly, Necessity arms us for all Employments.

My Cargo, as near as I can collect, for I have not kept an Account of the Particulars, consisted of a sufficient Quantity of Linnen, and some thin *English* Stuffs for cloathing the *Spaniards* that I expected to find there, and enough of them, as by my Calculation might comfortably supply them for seven Years; if I remember right, the Materials I carry'd for cloathing them with, Gloves, Hats Shoes, Stockings, and all such Things as they could want for wearing, amounted to above 200 Pounds, including some Beds, Bedding, and Houshold-Stuff, particularly Kitchen-Utensils, with Pots, Kettles, Peuter, Brass, *&c.*

and near a hundred Pound more in Iron-Work, Nails, Tools of every Kind, Staples, Hooks, Hinges, and every necessary Thing I could think of.

I carry'd also an hundred spare Arms, Muskets, and Fuzees, besides some Pistols, a considerable Quantity of Shot of all Sizes, and two Pieces of Brass Cannon; and because I knew not what Time, and what Extremities I was providing for, I carried an hundred Barrels of Powder, besides Swords, Cutlasses, and the Iron Part of some Pikes, and Halberts; so that in short we had a large Magazine of all Sorts of Stores; and I made my Nephew carry two small Quarter-Deck Guns more than he wanted for his Ship, to leave behind, if there was Occasion; that when we came there, we might build a Fort, and man it against all Sorts of Enemies: And indeed, I at first thought there was Need enough for it all, and much more, if we hop'd to maintain our Possession of the Island, as shall be seen in the Course of that Story.

I had not such bad Luck in this Voyage as I had been used to meet with; and therefore shall have the less Occasion to interrupt the Reader, who perhaps may be impatient to hear how Matters went with my Colony; yet some odd Accidents, cross Winds, and bad Weather happen'd, on this first setting out, which made the Voyage longer than I expected it at first; and I who had never made but one Voyage, (*viz.*) *my first Voyage to Guinea*, in which I might be said to come back again, as the Voyage was at first designed, began to think the same ill Fate still attended me; and that I was born to be never contented with being on Shore, and yet to be always unfortunate at Sea.

Contrary Winds first put us to the Northward, and we were oblig'd to put in at *Galway* in *Ireland*, where we lay Wind-bound two and twenty Days; but we had this Satisfaction with the Disaster, that Provisions were here exceeding cheap, and in the utmost Plenty; so that while we lay here, never touch'd the Ship's Stores, but rather added to them; here also I took in several live Hogs, and two Cows, and Calves, which I resolv'd, if I had a good Passage, to put on Shore in my Island, but we found Occasion to dispose otherwise of them.

We set out the 5th of *February* from *Ireland*, and had a very fair Gale of Wind for some Days. As I remember, it might be about the 20th of *February* in the Evening late, when the Mate having the Watch, came into the Round-house, and told us, he saw a Flash of Fire, and heard a Gun fir'd, and while he was telling us of it, a Boy came in, and told us the Boatswain heard another. This made us all run out upon the Quarter-Deck, where for a while we heard nothing, but in a few Minutes we saw a very great Light, and found that there was some very terrible Fire at a Distance; immediately we had Recourse to our Reckonings, in which we all agreed, that there could be no Land that Way, in which the Fire shew'd it self, no not for 500 Leagues, for it appear'd at W.N.W. Upon this we concluded it must be some Ship on Fire at Sea; and as by our hearing the Noise of Guns just before, we concluded it could not be far off: We stood directly towards it, and were presently satisfy'd we should discover it, because the farther we sail'd, the greater the Light appear'd, tho' the Weather being haizy, we could not perceive any Thing but the Light for a while; in about half an Hour's Sailing, the Wind being fair for us, tho' not much of it, and the Weather clearing up a little, we could plainly discern that it was a great Ship on fire in the Middle of the Sea.

I was most sensible touch'd with this Disaster tho' not

R. Crusoe saves the Crew of a Ship that took fire at Sea

at all acquainted with the Persons engag'd in it; I presently recollected my former Circumstances, and in what Condition I was in, when taken up by the *Portugal* Captain; and how much more deplorable the Circumstances of the poor Creatures belonging to this Ship must be, if they had no other Ship in Company with them: Upon this, I immediately order'd, that five Guns should be fir'd, one soon after another, that, if possible, we might give Notice to them, that there was Help for them at hand, and that they might endeavour to save themselves in their Boat; for tho' we could see the Flame of the Ship, yet they, it being Night, could see nothing of us.

We lay by some Time upon this, only driving as the burning Ship drove, waiting for Day-Light; when, on a sudden, to our great Terror, tho' we had Reason to expect it, the Ship blew up in the Air; and immediately, that is to say, in a few Minutes, all the Fire was out, that is to say, the rest of the Ship sunk: This was a terrible, and indeed an afflicting Sight, for the Sake of the poor Men, who, I concluded, must be either all destroy'd in the Ship, or be in the utmost Distress in their Boat in the Middle of the Ocean, which at present, by Reason it was dark, I could not see: However, to direct them as well as I could, I caused Lights to be hung out in all the Parts of the Ship where we could, and which we had Lanthorns for, and kept firing Guns all the Night long, letting them know by this, that there was a Ship not far off.

About 8 a Clock in the Morning we discover'd the Ship's Boats by the Help of our Perspective Glasses, found there were two of them, both throng'd with People, and deep in the Water: We perceived they row'd, the Wind being against them, that they saw our Ship, and did their utmost to make us see them.

We immediately spread our Antient to let them know we saw them, and hung a Waft out as a Signal for them to come on Board, and then made more Sail, standing directly to them. In little more than half an Hour we came up with them and, in a word, took them all in, being no less than sixty four Men, Women, and Children; for there were a great many Passengers.

Upon the whole, we found it was a *French* Merchant Ship of 300 Tun, homeward bound from *Quebeck*, in the River of *Canada*. The Master gave us a long Account of the Distress of his Ship, how the Fire began in the Steerage by the Negligence of the Steersman; but on his crying out for Help, was, as every Body thought, entirely put out, when they found that some Sparks of the first Fire had gotten into some Part of the Ship, so difficult to come at, that they could not effectually quench it, till getting in between the Timbers, and within the Ceiling of the Ship, it proceeded into the Hold, and master'd all the Skill, and all the Application they were able to exert.

They had no more to do then, but to get into their Boats, which to their great Comfort were pretty large, being their Long-Boat, and a great Shalloup, besides a small Skiff which was of no great Service to them, other than to get some fresh Water and Provisions in to her, after they had secur'd their Lives from the Fire. They had indeed small Hope of their Lives by getting into these Boats at that Distance from any Land, only as they said well, that they were escap'd from the Fire, and had a Possibility that some Ship might happen to be at Sea, and might take them in. They had Sails, Oars, and a Compass, and were preparing to make the best of their Way back to *New-found-Land*, the Wind blowing pretty fair, for it blew an easy Gale at S. E. by E. They had as much Provisions and

Water, as with sparing it so as to be next door to starving, might support them about 12 Days; in which, if they had no bad Weather, and no contrary Winds, the Captain said, he hop'd he might get the Banks of *Newfound-Land*, and might perhaps take some Fish to sustain them till they might go on Shore. But there were so many Chances against them in all these Cases; such as, Storms to overset and founder them, Rains and Cold to benumb and perish their Limbs, contrary Winds to keep them out and starve them, that it must have been next to miraculous if they had escap'd.

In the midst of their Consultations, every one being hopeless, and ready to despair, the Captain with Tears in his Eyes told me, they were on a sudden surpriz'd with the Joy of hearing a Gun fire, and after that four more; these were the five Guns which I caused to be fired at first seeing the Light: This reviv'd their Hearts, and gave them the Notice, which, *as above*, I desir'd it should, (*viz.*) that there was a Ship at hand for their Help.

It was upon the hearing these Guns, that they took down their Masts and Sails; the Sound coming from the Windward, they resolv'd to lye by till Morning. Some Time after this, hearing no more Guns, they fir'd three Muskets, one a considerable While after another; but these, the Wind being contrary, we never heard.

Some Time after that again, they were still more agreeably surpriz'd with seeing our Lights, and hearing the Guns, which, as I have said, I caus'd to be fir'd all the rest of the Night; this set them to work with their Oars to keep their Boats a-head, at least, that we might the sooner come up with them; and at last, to their inexpressible Joy, they found we saw them.

It is impossible for me to express the several Gestures,

the strange Extasies, the Variety of Postures which these poor deliver'd People run into, to express the Joy of their Souls at so unexpected a Deliverance; Grief and Fear are easily described; Sighs, Tears, Groans, and a very few Motions of the Head and Hands make up the Sum of its Variety: But an Excess of Joy, a Surprize of Joy has a Thousand Extravagancies in it; there were some in Tears, some raging, and tearing themselves, as if they had been in the greatest Agonies of Sorrow, some stark-raving and down-right lunatick, some ran about the Ship stamping with their Feet, others wringing their Hands; some were dancing, some singing, some laughing, more crying; many quite dumb, not able to speak a Word; others sick and vomiting, several swooning, and ready to faint; and a few were Crossing themselves, and giving God Thanks.

I would not wrong them neither, there might be many that were thankful afterward, but the Passion was too strong for them at first, and they were not able to master it, they were thrown into Extasies and a Kind of Frenzy, and it was but a very few that were compos'd and serious in their Joy.

Perhaps the Case may have some Addition to it from the particular Circumstance of that Nation they belong'd to, I mean the *French*, whose Temper is allow'd to be more volatile, more passionate, and more sprightly, and their Spirits more fluid than in other Nations. I am not Philosopher enough to determine the Cause, but nothing I had ever seen before came up to it: The Extasies poor *Friday*, my trusty *Savage*, was in when he found his Father in the Boat, came the nearest to it, and the Surprize of the Master and his two Companions, who I deliver'd from the Villains that set them on Shore in the Island, came a little Way towards it, but nothing was to compare to this, either that I saw in *Friday*, or any where else in my Life.

It is further observable, that these Extravagancies did not shew themselves in that different Manner I have mention'd in different Persons only: But all the Variety would appear in a short Succession of Moments in one and the same Person. A Man that we saw this Minute dumb, and as it were stupid and confounded, should the next Minute be dancing and hallowing like an Antick; and the next Moment be tearing his Hair, or pulling his Clothes to Pieces, and stamping them under his Feet, like a mad Man; a few Moments after that, we should have him all in Tears, then sick, then swooning, and had not immediate Help been had, would, in a few Moments more have been dead; and thus it was not with one or two, or ten or twenty, but with the greatest Part of them; and if I remember right, our Surgeon was oblig'd to let above thirty of them Blood.

There were two Priests among them, one an old Man, and the other a young Man; and that which was strangest was, that the oldest Man was the worst. As soon as he set his Foot on board our Ship, and saw himself safe, he dropt done stone-dead, not the least Sign of Life could be perceiv'd in him; our Surgeon immediately apply'd proper Remedies to recover him, and was the only Man in the Ship that believ'd he was not dead; at length he open'd a Vein in his Arm, having first chaff'd and rubb'd the Part so as to warm it as much as possible: Upon this the Blood which only dropp'd at first, flow'd something freely; in three Minutes after, the Man open'd his Eyes, and about a quarter of an Hour after that he spoke, grew better, and quite well; after the Blood was stopp'd he walk'd about, told us he was perfectly well, took a Dram of

Cordial which the Surgeon gave him, and was what we call'd, *Come to himself*; about a quarter of an Hour after they came running into the Cabin to the Surgeon, who was bleeding a *French* Woman, that had fainted; and told him, the Priest was gone stark-mad; it seems he had begun to revolve the Change of his Circumstance, and again this put him into an Extasy of Joy, his Spirits whirl'd about faster than the Vessels could convey them; the Blood grew hot and feverish, and the Man was as fit for *Bedlam* as any Creature that ever was in it; the Surgeon would not bleed him again in that Condition, but gave him something to dose and put him to sleep, which after some Time operated upon him, and he wak'd the next Morning perfectly compos'd and well.

The younger Priest behav'd with great Command of his Passion, and was really an Example of a serious well-govern'd Mind; at his first coming on board the Ship, he threw himself flat on his Face, prostrating himself in Thankfulness for his Deliverance, in which I unhappily and unseasonably disturb'd him, really thinking he had been in a Swoon; but he spake calmly, thank'd me, told me he was giving God Thanks for his Deliverance, and begg'd me to leave him a few Moments, and that, next to his Maker, he would give me Thanks also.

I was heartily sorry, that I disturb'd him, and not only left him, but kept others from interrupting him also; he continued in that Posture about three Minutes, or little more, after I left him, then came to me, as he had said he would, and with a great deal of Seriousness and Affection, but with Tears in his Eyes, thank'd me that had under God, given him and so many miserable Creatures their Lives: I told him, I had no Room to move him to thank God for it, rather than me: But I added, That it was nothing but what Reason and Humanity dictated to all Men, and that we had as much Reason as he to give Thanks to God, who had bless'd us so far as to make us the Instruments of his Mercy to so many of his Creatures.

After this, the young Priest apply'd himself to his Country-Folks; labour'd to compose them; perswaded, entreated, argued, reason'd with them, and did his utmost to keep them within the Exercise of their Reason; and with some he had Success, tho' others were for a Time out of all Government of themselves.

I cannot help committing this to Writing, as perhaps it may be useful to those into whose Hands it may fall, for the guiding themselves in all the Extravagances of their Passions; for if an Excess of Joy can carry Men out to such a Length beyond the Reach of their Reason, what will not the Extravagancies of Anger, Rage, and a provok'd Mind carry us to? and indeed here I saw Reason for keeping an exceeding Watch over our Passions of every Kind, as well those of Joy and Satisfaction, as those of Sorrow and Anger.

We were something disordered by these Extravagancies among our new Guests for the first Day, but when they had been retir'd, Lodgings provided for them as well as our Ship would allow, and they had slept heartily, as most of them did, they were quite another Sort of People the next Day.

Nothing of good Manners or civil Acknowledgments for the Kindness shewn them was wanting; the *French*, 'tis known, are naturally apt enough to exceed that Way. The Captain and one of the Priests came to me the next Day, and desiring to speak with me and my Nephew, the Commander, began to consult with us what should be done with them; and first they told us, that as we had saved their Lives, so all they had was little enough for a Return to us for that Kindness received. The Captain said, they had saved some Money and some Things of Value in their Boats, catch'd hastily out of the Flames, and if we would accept it, they were ordered to make an Offer of it all to us; they only desired to be set on Shore somewhere in our Way, where if possible they might get Passage to *France*.

My Nephew was for accepting their Money at first Word, and to consider what to do with them afterwards; but I over-rul'd him in that Part, for I knew what it was to be set on Shore in a strange Country; and if the *Portugal* Captain that took me up at Sea had serv'd me so, and took all I had for my Deliverance, I must have starv'd, or have been as much a Slave at the *Brasils* as I had been in *Barbary*, the meer being sold to a *Mahometan* excepted; and perhaps a *Portuguese* is not much a better Master than a *Turk*, if not in some Cases a much worse.

I therefore told the *French* Captain that we had taken them up in their Distress, it was true; but that it was our Duty to do so as we were Fellow-Creatures, and as we would desire to be so deliver'd if we were in the like or any other Extremity; that we had done nothing for them but what we believed they would have done for us, if we had been in their Case, and they in ours; but that we took them up to save them, not to plunder them; and it would be a most barbarous thing to take that little from them which they saved out of the Fire, and then set them on Shore and leave them; that this would be first to save them from Death, and then kill them our selves; save them from drowning, and abandon them to starving; and therefore I would not let the least thing be taken from them: As to setting them on Shore, I told them indeed that was an exceeding Difficulty to us, for that the Ship was bound to the *East-Indies*; and tho' we were driven out of our Course to the Westward a very great Way, and perhaps was directed by Heaven on Purpose for their Deliverance, yet it was impossible for us wilfully to change our Voyage on this particular Account, nor could my Nephew, the Captain, answer it to the Freighters, with whom he was under Charter-Party to pursue his Voyage by the Way of *Brasil*, and all I knew we could do for them, was to put our selves in the Way of meeting with other Ships homeward bound from the *West-Indies*, and get them Passage, if possible, to *England* or *France*.

The first Part of the Proposal was so generous and kind, they could not but be very thankful for it; but they were in a very great Consternation, especially the Passengers, at the Notion of being carry'd away to the *East-Indies*, and they then entreated me, that seeing I was driven so far to the Westward, before I met with them, I would at least keep on the same Course to the Banks of *Newfound-Land*, where it was probable I might meet with some Ship or Sloop that they might hire to carry them back to *Canada*, from whence they came.

I thought this was but a reasonable Request on their Part, and therefore I enclin'd to agree to it; for indeed I consider'd, that to carry this whole Company to the *East-Indies*, would not only be an intolerable Severity upon the poor People, but would be ruining our whole Voyage by devouring all our Provisions; so I thought it no Breach of Charter-Party, but what an unforeseen Accident made absolutely necessary to us, and in which no one could say we were to blame; for the Laws of God and Nature would have forbid that we should refuse to take up two Boats full of People in such a distress'd Condition, and the Nature of the Thing as well respecting our selves as the poor

People, oblig'd us to set them on Shore some where or other for their Deliverance; so I consented that we would carry them to *Newfound-Land*, if Wind and Weather would permit, and if not, that I would carry them to *Martinico* in the *West-Indies*.

The Wind continued fresh Easterly, but the Weather pretty good, and as the Winds had continued in the Points between N. E. and S. E. a long time, we missed several Opportunities of sending them to *France*; for we met several Ships bound to *Europe*, whereof two were *French* from St. *Christopher's*, but they had been so long beating up against the Wind, that they durst take in no Passengers for fear of wanting Provisions for the Voyage, as well for themselves as for those they should take in; so we were obliged to go on. It was about a Week after this that we made the Banks of *Newfound-Land*, where to shorten my Story, we put all our *French* People on Board a Bark, which they hir'd at Sea there, to put them on Shore, and afterwards to carry them to *France*, if they could get Provision to victual themselves with. When, I say, all the *French* went on Shore, I should remember that the young Priest I spoke of, hearing we were bound to the *East Indies*, desired to go the Voyage with us, and to be set on Shore on the Coast of *Coromandel*, which I readily agreed to, for I wonderfully lik'd the Man, and had very good Reason, as will appear afterwards; also four of the Seamen entered themselves on our Ship, and proved very useful Fellows.

From hence we directed our Course for the *West-Indies*, steering away S. and S. by E. for about twenty Days together, sometimes little or no Wind at all, when we met with another Subject for our Humanity to work upon, almost as deplorable as that before.

It was in the Latitude of 27 Degrees 5 Minutes North, and the 19th Day of *March* 1694-5, when we 'spy'd a Sail, our Course S. E. and by S. We soon perceiv'd it was a large Vessel, and that she bore up to us, but could not at first know what to make of her, till after coming a little nearer, we found she had lost her Main-top-mast, Fore-mast and Boltsprit, and presently she fired a Gun as a Signal of Distress; the Weather was pretty good, Wind at N. N. W. a fresh Gale, and we soon came to speak with her.

We found her a Ship of *Bristol*, bound home from *Barbadoes*, but had been blown out of the Road at *Barbadoes* a few Days before she was ready to sail, by a terrible Hurricane, while the Captain and Chief Mate were both gone on Shore, so that beside the Terror of the Storm, they were but in an indifferent Case for good Artists to bring the Ship home: They had been already nine Weeks at Sea, and had met with another terrible Storm after the Hurricane was over, which had blown them quite out of their Knowledge to the Westward, and in which they lost their Masts, as above; they told us they expected to have seen the *Bahama* Islands, but were then driven away again to the South East by a strong Gale of Wind at N. N. W. the same that blew now, and having no Sails to work the Ship with but a main Course, and a kind of square Sail upon a Jury Fore-mast, which they had set up, they could not lye near the Wind, but were endeavouring to stand away for the *Canaries*.

But that which was worst of all, was, that they were almost starv'd for want of Provisions, besides the Fatigues they had undergone; their Bread and Flesh was quite gone, they had not one Ounce left in the Ship, and had had none for eleven Days; the only Relief they had, was, their Water was not all spent, and they had about half a Barrel of Flower left; they had Sugar enough; some Succades, or Sweet-meats they had at first, but they were devour'd, and they had seven Casks of Rum.

There was a Youth and his Mother and a Maid-Servant on Board, who were going Passengers, and thinking the Ship was ready to sail, unhappily came on Board the Evening before the Hurricane began, and having no Provisions of their own left, they were in a more deplorable Condition than the rest, for the Seamen being reduced to such an extreme Necessity themselves, had no Compassion, we may be sure, for the poor Passengers, and they were indeed in a Condition that their Misery is very hard to describe.

I had, perhaps, not known this Part, if my Curiosity had not led me, the Weather being fair and the Wind abated, to go on Board the Ship: The Second Mate who upon this Occasion commanded the Ship, had been on Board our Ship, and he told me indeed they had three Passengers in the great Cabin, that they were in a deplorable Condition; nay, says he, I believe they are dead, for I have heard nothing of them for above two Days, and I was afraid to enquire after them, said he, for I had nothing to relieve them with.

We immediately apply'd our selves to give them what Relief we could spare; and indeed I had so far over-ruled Things with my Nephew, that I would have victuall'd them, tho' we had gone away to *Virginia*, or any Part of the Coast of *America*, to have supply'd our selves; but there was no Necessity for that.

But now they were in a new Danger; for they were afraid of eating too much, even of that little we gave them; the Mate or Commander brought six Men with him in his

Boat, but these poor Wretches look'd like Skeletons, and were so weak, they could hardly sit to their Oars: The Mate himself was very ill, and half ſtarv'd; for he declar'd he had reserv'd nothing from the Men, and went Share and Share alike with them in every Bit they eat.

I caution'd him to eat sparingly, but set Meat before him immediately, and he had not eaten three Mouthfuls before he began to be Sick, and out of Order; so he ſtopt a while, and our Surgeon mix'd him up something with some Broth, which he said would be to him both Food and Physick; and after he had taken it, he grew better: In the mean Time, I forgot not the Men; I order'd Victuals to be given them, and the poor Creatures rather devour'd than eat it; they were so exceeding hungry, that they were in a kind ravenous, and had no Command of themselves; and two of them eat with so much Greediness, that they were in Danger of their Lives the next Morning.

The Sight of these People's Diſtress was very moving to me, and brought to Mind what I had a terrible Prospect of at my firſt coming on Shore in the Island, where I had neither the leaſt Mouthful of Food, or any Prospect of procuring any; besides the hourly Apprehension I had of being made the Food of other Creatures: But all the while the Mate was thus relating to me the miserable Condition of the Ship's Company, I could not put out of my Thought the Story he had told me of the three poor Creatures in the Great Cabin, (*viz.*) the Mother, her Son, and the Maid-servant, who he had heard nothing of for two or three Days, and who he seem'd to confess they had wholly neglected, their own Extremities being so great; by which I underſtood, that they had really given them no Food at all, and that therefore they muſt be perish'd, and be all lying dead perhaps on the Floor, or Deck of the Cabin.

As I therefore kept the Mate, who we then called Captain, on board with his Men to refresh them, so I also forgot not the starving Crew that were left on board, but order'd my own Boat to go on board the Ship, and with my Mate and twelve Men to carry them a Sack of Bread, and four or five Pieces of Beef to boil. Our Surgeon charg'd the Men to cause the Meat to be boil'd while they stay'd, and to keep Guard in the Cook-Room, to prevent the Men taking it to eat raw, or taking it out of the Pot before it was well boil'd, and then to give every Man but a very little at a Time; and by this Caution he preserv'd the Men, who would otherwise ha' kill'd themselves with that very Food that was given them on Purpose to save their Lives.

At the same Time, I order'd the Mate to go into the Great Cabin, and see what Condition the poor Passengers were in, and if they were alive, to comfort them, and give them what Refreshment was proper; and the Surgeon gave him a large Pitcher with some of the prepar'd Broth which he had given the Mate that was on board, and which he did not question would restore them gradually.

I was not satisfy'd with this, but as I said above, having a great Mind to see the Scene of Misery, which I knew the Ship itself would present me with, in a more lively Manner than I could have it by Report, I took the Captain of the Ship, as we now call'd him, with me, and went myself a little after in their Boat.

I found the poor Men on board almost in a Tumult to get the Victuals out of the Boyler before it was ready: But my Mate observ'd his Order, and kept a good Guard at the Cook-Room Door, and the Man he plac'd there, after using all possible Perswasion to have Patience, kept them off by Force: However, he caused some Bisket Cakes to be dipp'd in the Pot, and soften'd with the Liquor of the Meat, which they call Brews, and gave them every one, one, to stay their Stomachs, and told them it was for their own Safety that he was oblig'd to give them but a little at a Time: But it was all in vain; and had I not come on Board, and their own Commander and Officers with me, and with good Words, and some Threats also of giving them no more, I believe they would have broke into the Cook-Room by Force, and tore the Meat out of the Furnace: For Words are indeed of very small Force to a hungry Belly: However we pacify'd them, and fed them gradually and cautiously for the first Time, and the next Time gave them more, and at last fill'd their Bellies, and the Men did well enough.

But the Misery of the poor Passengers in the Cabin, was of another Nature, and far beyond the rest; for as first the Ship's Company had so little for themselves, it was but too true that they had at first kept them very low, and at last totally neglected them; so that for six or seven Days, it might be said, they had really had no Food at all, and for several Days before very little. The poor Mother, who as the Men reported, was a Woman of good Sense and good Breeding, had spar'd all she could get, so affectionately for her Son, that at last she entirely sunk under it: And when the Mate of our Ship went in, she sat upon the Floor or Deck, with her Back up against the Sides, between two Chairs, which were lash'd fast, and her Head sunk in between her Shoulders, like a Corpse, tho' not quite dead. My Mate said all he could to revive and encourage her, and with a Spoon put some Broth into her Mouth; she open'd her Lips, and lifted up one Hand, but could not speak; yet she understood what he said, and made Signs to him, intimating, that it was too late for her, but pointed to her Child, as if she would have said, they should take Care of him.

However, the Mate, who was exceedingly mov'd with the Sight, endeavour'd to get some of the Broth into her Mouth; and as he said, got two or three Spoonfuls down, tho' I question whether he could be sure of it or not: But it was too late, and she dy'd the same Night.

The Youth who was preserved at the Price of his most affectionate Mother's Life, was not so far gone, yet he lay in a Cabin-bed as one stretch'd out, with hardly any Life left in him; he had a Piece of an old Glove in his Mouth, having eaten up the rest of it; however, being young, and having more Strength than his Mother, the Mate got something down his Throat, and he began sensibly to revive, tho' by giving him some time after but two or three Spoonfuls extraordinary, he was very sick, and brought it up again.

But the next Care was the poor Maid, she lay all along upon the Deck hard by her Mistress, and just like one that had fallen down with an Apoplexy and struggled for Life: Her Limbs were distorted, one of her Hands was clasp'd round the Frame of a Chair, and she grip'd it so hard, that we could not easily make her let go; her other Arm lay over her Head, and her Feet lay both together set fast against the Frame of the Cabin Table; in short, she lay just like one in the last Agonies of Death, and yet she was alive too.

The poor Creature was not only starv'd with Hunger, and terrify'd with the Thoughts of Death, but as the Men told us afterwards, was broken-hearted for her Mistress, who she saw dying for two or three Days before, and who she lov'd most tenderly.

We knew not what to do with this poor Girl, for when our Surgeon, who was a Man of very great Knowledge and Experience, had with great Application recover'd her as to Life; he had her upon his Hand as to her Senses, for she was little less than distracted for a considerable Time after, as shall appear presently.

Whoever shall read these *Memorandums* must be desir'd to consider, that Visits at Sea are not like a Journey into the Country, where sometimes People stay a Week or a Fortnight at a Place. Our Business was to relieve this distressed Ship's Crew, but not to lie by for them; and tho' they were willing to steer the same Course with us for some Days, yet we could carry no Sail to keep Pace with a Ship that had no Masts; however, as their Captain begg'd of us to help him to set up a Main-Top-Mast, and a Kind of a Top-Mast to his Jury Fore-Mast, we did, as it were lie by him for three or four Days, and then having given him five Barrels of Beef, a Barrel of Pork, two Hogsheads of Bisket, and a Proportion of Peas, Flour, and what other Things we could spare; and taking three Casks of Sugar, some Rum, and some Pieces of Eight of them for Satisfaction, we left them, taking on board with us, at their own earnest Request, the Priest, the Youth, and the Maid, and all their Goods.

The young Lad was about seventeen Years of Age, a pretty, well-bred modest, and sensible Youth, greatly dejected with the Loss of his Mother, and as it seems had lost his Father but a few Months before at *Berbadoes*. He begg'd of the Surgeon to speak to me to take him out of the Ship, for he said the cruel Fellows had murther'd his

Mother; *and indeed so they had*, that is to say *passively*; for they might ha' spar'd a small Suſtenance to the poor helpless Widow, that might have preserv'd her Life, tho' it had been but juſt to keep her alive. But Hunger knows no Friend, no Relation, no Juſtice, no Right, and therefore is remorseless, and capable of no Compassion.

The Surgeon told him how far we were going, and how it would carry him away from all his Friends, and put him perhaps in as bad Circumſtances almoſt as those we found him in; that is to say, ſtarving in the World: He said he matter'd not whether he went, if he was but delivered from the terrible Crew he was among: That the Captain (by which he meant me, for he could know nothing of my Nephew) had sav'd his Life, and he was sure would not hurt him; and as for the Maid, he was sure if she came to herself, she would be very thankful for it, let us carry them where we would. The Surgeon represented the Case so affectionately to me, that I yielded, and we took them both on board with all their Goods, except eleven Hogsheads of Sugar, which could not be removed or come at, and as the Youth had a Bill of Lading for them, I made his Commander sign a Writing, obliging himself to go as soon as he came to *Briſtol*, to one Mr. *Rogers* a Merchant there, to whom the Youth said he was related, and to deliver a Letter which I wrote to him, and all the Goods he had belonging to the deceased Widow; which I suppose was not done, for I could never learn that the Ship came to *Briſtol*, but was, as is moſt probable, loſt at Sea, being in so disabled a Condition and so far from any Land, that I am of Opinion, the firſt Storm she met with afterwards, she might founder in the Sea, for she was leaky, and had Damage in her Hold when we met with her.

I was now in the Latitude of 19 Deg. 32 Min. and had hitherto had a tolerable Voyage as to Weather, tho' at first the Winds had been contrary. I shall trouble no Body with the little Incidents of Wind, Weather, Currents, *&c.* on the rest of our Voyage; but shortning my Story for the sake of what is to follow, shall observe that I came to my old Habitation, the Island, on the 10th of *April* 1695. It was with no small Difficulty that I found the Place; for as I came to it, and went from it before, on the South and East Side of the Island, as coming from the *Brasils*, so now coming in between the Main and the Island, and having no Chart for the Coast, nor any Land-Mark, I did not know it when I saw it, or know whether I saw it or no.

We beat about a great while, and went on Shore on several Islands in the Mouth of the great River *Oronooque*, but none for my Purpose. Only this I learn'd by my Coasting the Shore, that I was under one great Mistake before, *viz.* that the Continent which I thought I saw, from the Island I liv'd in, was really no Continent, but a long Island, or rather a Ridge of Islands, reaching from one to the other Side of the extended Mouth of that great River, and that the Savages who came to my Island, were not properly those which we call *Caribbees*, but Islanders, and other Barbarians of the same Kind, who inhabited something nearer to our Side than the rest.

In short, I visited several of these Islands to no Purpose; some I found were inhabited, and some were not. On one of them I found some *Spaniards*, and thought they had liv'd there, but speaking with them, found they had a sloop lay in a small Creek hard by, and they came thither to make Salt, and to catch some Pearl Mussles if they could, but that they belong'd to the Isle *de Trinidad*, which lay farther North in the Latitude of 10 and 11 Degrees.

But at laſt coaſting from one Island to another, sometimes with the Ship, sometimes with the *French* Mans Shalloup, which we had found a convenient Boat, and therefore kept her with their very good Will; at length I came fair on the South Side of my Island, and I presently knew the very Countenance of the Place; so I brought the Ship safe to an Anchor, Broadside with the little Creek where was my old Habitation.

As soon as I saw the Place, I call'd for *Friday*, and ask'd him if he knew where he was? He look'd about a little, and presently clapping his Hands, cry'd; *O yes*, *O there*, *O yes*, *O there*, pointing to our old Habitation, and fell a dancing and capering like a mad Fellow, and I had much ado to keep him from jumping into the Sea, to swim ashore to the Place.

Well, *Friday*, says I, do you think we shall find any Body here or no? And what do you think, shall we see your Father? The Fellow ſtood mute as a Stock a good while, but when I nam'd his Father, the poor affectionate Creature look'd dejected, and I could see the Tears run down his Face very plentifully. What is the Matter, *Friday*, says I? Are you troubled because you may see your Father? No, no, *says he*, shaking his Head, no see him more, no ever more see again; *why so*, said I *Friday*, *how do you know that?* O no, O no, says *Friday*, he long ago die, long ago; he much old Man. Well, well, *says I*, *Friday*, you don't know; but shall we see any one else then? The Fellow, it seems, had better Eyes than I, and he points juſt to the Hill above my old House; and tho' we lay half a League off, he cries out, we see! we see! yes, we see much Men there, and there, and there. I look'd, but I could see no body, no not with a Perspective Glass, which was, I suppose, because I could not hit the Place, for the Fellow was right, as I found upon Enquiry the next Day, and there was five or six Men altogether, stood to look at the Ship, not knowing what to think of us.

As soon as *Friday* had told me he saw People, I caus'd the *English* Antient to be spread, and fir'd three Guns, to give them Notice we were Friends, and in about half a Quarter of an Hour after, we perceiv'd a Smoke rise from the Side of the Creek, so I immediately order'd a Boat out taking *Friday* with me, and hanging out a white Flag, or, Flag of Truce, I went directly on Shore, taking with me the young Fryer I mention'd, to whom I had told the whole Story of my living there, and the manner of it, and every Particular both of my self, and those I left there; and who was on that Account extremely desirous to go with me. We had besides about sixteen Men very well arm'd, if we had found any new Guests there which we did not know of; but we had no Need of Weapons.

As we went on Shore upon the Tide of Flood, near high Water, we row'd directly into the Creek, and the first Man I fix'd my Eye upon, was the *Spaniard* whose Life I had sav'd, and who I knew by his Face perfectly well; as to his Habit I shall describe it afterwards. I order'd no body to go on Shore at first but my self, but there was no keeping *Friday* in the Boat; for the affectionate Creature had spy'd his Father at a Distance, a good Way off of the *Spaniards*, where indeed I saw nothing of him; and if they had not let him go on Shore, he would have jump'd into the Sea. He was no sooner on Shore, but he flew away to his Father like an Arrow out of a Bow. It would have made any Man have shed Tears in Spight of the firmest Resolution, to have seen the first Transports of this poor Fellow's Joy when he came to his Father; how he embrac'd him, kiss'd him, strok'd his Face, took him up in his Arms, set him down upon a Tree, and lay down by him, then stood and look'd at him, as any one would look at a strange Picture for a Quarter of an Hour together; then lye down on the Ground, and stroke his Legs, and kiss them, and then get up again, and stare at him; one would ha' thought the Fellow bewitch'd: But it would ha' made a Dog laugh to see how the next Day his Passion run out another Way: In the Morning he walk'd along the Shore, to and again, with his Father several Hours, always leading him by the Hand, as if he had been a Lady; and every now and then he would come to fetch something or other for him to the Boat, either a Lump of Sugar, or a Dram, a Bisket Cake, or something or other that was good. In the Afternoon his Frolicks run another Way; for then he would set the old Man down upon the Ground, and dance about him, and make a Thousand antick Postures and Gestures; and all the while he did this, he would be talking to him, and telling him one Story or another of his Travels, and of what had happen'd to him Abroad, to divert him. In short, if the same filial Affection was to be found in Christians to their Parents, in our Part of the World, one would be tempted to say, there would hardly ha' been any Need of the Fifth Commandment.

But this is a Digression; I return to my Landing. It would be endless to take Notice of all the Ceremonies and Civilities that the *Spaniards* receiv'd me with. The first *Spaniard*, who, as I said, I knew very well, was he whose Life I had sav'd; he came towards the Boat, attended by one more, carrying a Flag of Truce also; and he did not only not know me at first, but he had no Thoughts, no

Notion of its being me that was come, till I spoke to him: Seignior, said I in *Portuguese*, Do you not know me? At which he spoke not a Word; but giving his Musket to the Man that was with him, threw his Arms abroad, and saying something in *Spanish*, that I did not perfectly hear, comes forward, and embrac'd me, telling me he was inexcusable, not to know that Face again, that he had once seen, as of an Angel from Heaven sent to save his Life: He said Abundance of very handsome Things, as a well bred *Spaniard* always knows how; and then beckoning to the Person that attended him, bad him go and call out his Comerades. He then ask'd me, if I would walk to my old Habitation, where he would give me Possession of my own House again, and where I should see there had been but mean Improvements; so I walk'd along with him; but alas I could no more find the Place again, than if I had never been there; for they had planted so many Trees, and plac'd them in such a Posture, so thick and close to one another; and in ten Years Time they were grown so big, that *in short* the Place was inaccessible, except by such Windings and blind Ways, as they themselves only, who made them, could find.

I ask'd them what put them upon all these Fortifications? He told me, I would say there was Need enough of it, when they had given me an Account how they had pass'd their Time since their Arriving in the Island, especially after they had the Misfortune to find that I was gone: He told me, he could not but have some Satisfaction in my good Fortune, when he heard that I was gone away in a good Ship, and to my Satisfaction; and that he had often-times a strong Perswasion, that one Time or other he should see me again: But nothing that ever befel him in his Life, he said, was so surprizing and afflicting to him at first, as the Disappointment he was under when he came back to the Island, and found I was not there.

As to the three *Barbarians* (so he call'd them) that were left behind, and of whom he said he had a long Story to tell me; the *Spaniards* all thought themselves much better among the Savages, only that their Number was so small. And, says he, had they been strong enough, we had been all long ago in Purgatory; and with that he cross'd himself on the Breast: But Sir, says he, I hope you will not be displeas'd, when I shall tell you how forc'd by Necessity we were oblig'd, for our own Preservation, to disarm them, and make them our Subjects, who would not be content with being moderately our Masters, but would be our Murtherers. I answer'd, I was heartily afraid of it when I left them there; and nothing troubled me at my parting from the Island, but that they were not come back, that I might have put them in Possession of every Thing first, and left the other in a State of Subjection, as they deserv'd: But if they had reduc'd them to it, I was very glad, and should be very far from finding any Fault with it; for I knew they were a Parcel of refractory, ungovern'd Villains, and were fit for any Manner of Mischief.

While I was saying this, came the Man whom he had sent back, and with him eleven Men more: In the Dress they were in, it was impossible to guess what Nation they were of: But he made all clear both to them and to me. First he turn'd to me, and pointing to them, said, These, Sir, are some of the Gentlemen who owe their Lives to you; and then turning to them, and pointing to me, he let them know who I was; upon which they all came up one by one, not as if they had been Sailors and ordinary Fellows, and I the like, but really, as if they had been Ambassadors of Noblemen, and I a Monarch or a great Conqueror; their Behaviour was to the last Degree obliging and courteous, and yet mix'd with a Manly, Majestick Gravity, which very well became them; and in short, they had so much more Manners than I, that I scarce knew how to receive their Civilities, much less how to return them in Kind.

The History of their coming to, and Conduct in the Island, after my going away, is so very remarkable, and has so many Incidents, which the former Part of my Relation will help to understand, and which will in most of the Particulars, refer to that Account I have already given, that I cannot but commit them with great Delight to the reading of those that come after me.

I shall no longer trouble the Story with a Relation in the first Person, which will put me to the Expence of ten Thousand *said I's*, and *said he's*, and he *told me's*, and I *told him's*, and the like, but I shall collect the Facts Historically, as near as I can gather them out of my Memory from what they related to me, and from what I met with in my conversing with them and with the Place.

In Order to do this succinctly, and as intelligibly as I can, I must go back to the Circumstance in which I left the Island, and in which the Persons were of whom I am to speak. And first it is necessary to repeat, that I had sent away *Friday's* Father and the *Spaniard*, the two whose Lives I had rescued from the Savages, I say, I had sent them away in a large Canoe to the Main, *as I then thought it*, to fetch over the *Spaniard's* Companions who he had left behind him, in order to save them from the like Calamity that he had been in; and in order to succour them for the present, and that if possible, we might together find some Way for our Deliverance afterward.

When I sent them away, I had no visible Appearance

of, or the least Room to hope for my own Deliverance any more than I had twenty Year before, much less had I any Fore-knowledge of what afterward happened, I mean of an *English* Ship coming on Shore there to fetch me off; and it could not but be a very great Surprize to them when they came back, not only to find that I was gone, but to find three Strangers left on the Spot, possess'd of all that I had left behind me, which would otherwise have been their own.

The first Thing, however, which I enquir'd into, that I might begin where I left off, was of their own Part; and I desir'd he would give me a particular Account of his Voyage back to his Countrymen with the Boat, when I sent him to fetch them over. He told me there was little Variety in that Part, for nothing remarkable happen'd to them on the Way, they having very calm Weather, and a smooth Sea; for his Countrymen it could not be doubted, he said, but that they were overjoy'd to see him: (It seems he was the principal Man among them, the Captain of the Vessel they had been shipwreck'd in, having been dead some Time) they were, *he said*, the more surprized to see him, because they knew that he was fallen into the Hands of the Savages, who, they were satisfy'd, would devour him as they did all the rest of the Prisoners, that when he told them the Story of his Deliverance, and in what Manner he was furnish'd for carrying them away, it was like a Dream to them; and their Astonishment, they said, was something like that of *Joseph's* Brethren, when he told them who he was, and told them the Story of his Exaltation in *Pharaoh's* Court: But when he shewed them the Arms, the Powder, the Ball, and the Provisions that he brought them for their Journey or Voyage, they were restor'd to themselves, took a just Share of the Joy of their

Deliverance, and immediately prepar'd to come away with him.

Their first Business was to get Canoes; and in this they were obliged not to stick so much upon the honest Part of it, but to trespass upon their friendly Savages, and to borrow two large Canoes, or Periagua's, on Pretence of going out a Fishing, or for Pleasure.

In these they came away the next Morning; it seems they wanted no Time to get themselves ready; for they had no Baggage, neither Clothes or Provisions, or any Thing in the World, but what they had on them, and a few Roots to eat, of which they used to make their Bread.

They were in all three Weeks absent, and in that Time, unluckily for them, I had the Occasion offer'd for my Escape, as I mention'd in my other Part, and to get off from the Island, leaving three of the most impudent, harden'd, ungovern'd, disagreeable Villains behind me, that any Man could desire to meet with, to the poor *Spaniards* great Grief and Disappointment, you may be sure.

The only just Thing the Rogues did, was, That when the *Spaniards* came on Shore, they gave my Letter to them, and gave them Provisions and other Relief, as I had ordered them to do; also they gave them the long Paper of Directions which I had left with them, containing the particular Methods which I took for managing every Part of my Life there, the Way how I baked my Bread, bred up tame Goats, and planted my Corn, how I cur'd my Grapes, made my Pots, and, in a Word, every Thing I did, all this being written down, they gave to the *Spaniards*, two of whom understand *English* well enough; nor did they refuse to accommodate the *Spaniards* with every Thing else, for they agreed very well for some Time; they gave them an equal Admission into the House, or

Cave, and they began to live very sociably, and the Head *Spaniard*, who had seen pretty much of my Methods, and *Friday's* Father together, manag'd all their Affairs; for, as for the *English* Men, they did nothing but ramble about the Island, shoot Parrots, and catch Tortoises, and when they came Home at Night, the *Spaniards* provided their Suppers for them.

The *Spaniards* would have been satisfy'd with this, would the other but have let them alone, which, however, they could not find in their Hearts to do long; but, like the Dog in the Manger, they would not eat themselves, and would not let others eat neither: The Differences, nevertheless, were at first but trivial, and such as are not worth relating; but at last, it broke out into open War, and it begun with all the Rudeness and Insolence that can be imagin'd, without Reason, without Provocation, contrary to Nature, and indeed, to common Sense; and tho' it is true the first Relation of it came from the *Spaniards* themselves, who I may call the Accusers, yet when I came to examine the Fellows, they could not deny a Word of it.

But before I come to the Particulars of this Part, I must supply a Defect in my former Relation, and this was, that I forgot to set down among the rest, that just as we were weighing the Anchor to set Sail, there happen'd a little Quarrel on board our Ship, which I was afraid once would have turn'd to a second Mutiny; nor was it appeas'd, till the Captain rouzing up his Courage, and taking us all to his Assistance, parted them by Force, and making two of the most refractory Fellows Prisoners, he laid them in Irons, and as they had been active in the former Disorders, and let fall some ugly dangerous Words the second Time, he threaten'd to carry them in Irons to *England*,

and have them hang'd there for Mutiny, and running away with the Ship.

This, it seems, tho' the Captain did not intend to do it, frighted some other Men in the Ship, and some of them had put it into the Heads of the reſt, that the Captain only gave them good Words for the present, till they should come to some *English* Port, and that then they should be all put into Jayl, and try'd for their Lives.

The Mate got Intelligence of this, and acquainted us with it; upon which it was desir'd, that I, who ſtill pass'd for a great Man among them, should go down with the Mate, and satisfy the Men, and tell them, that they might be assur'd, if they behav'd well the reſt of the Voyage, all they had done for the Time paſt should be pardon'd. So I went, and after passing *my Honour's* Word to them, they appear'd easy; and the more so, when I caused the two Men who were in Irons, to be released and forgiven.

But this Mutiny had brought us to an Anchor for that Night, the Wind also falling calm, next Morning we found, that our two Men who had been laid in Irons, had ſtole each of them a Musket, and some other Weapons, what Powder or Shot they had, we know not; and had taken the Ship's Pinnace, which was not yet hal'd up, and ran way with her to their Companions in Roguery on Shore.

As soon as we found this, I order'd the Long-Boat on Shore, with twelve Men and the Mate, and away they went to seek the Rogues, but they could neither find them, or any of the reſt; for they all fled into the Woods when they saw the Boat coming on Shore. The Mate was once resolv'd, in Juſtice to their Roguery, to have deſtroy'd their Plantations, burnt all their Houshold-Stuff and Furniture, and left them to shift without it; but having no

Order, he let it all alone, left every Thing as they found it, and bringing the Pinnace away, came on board without them.

These two Men made their Number five, but the other three Villains were so much wickeder than these, that after they had been 2 or 3 Days together, they turn'd their two New-Comers out of Doors to shift for themselves, and would have nothing to do with them, nor could they for a good while be perswaded to give them any Food; as for the *Spaniards* they were not yet come.

When the *Spaniards* came first on Shore, the Business began to go forward; the *Spaniards* would have persuaded the three *English* Brutes to have taken in their two Countrymen again, that, as they said, they might be all one Family; but they would not hear of it: So the two poor Fellows liv'd by themselves, and finding nothing but Industry and Application would make them live comfortably, they pitch'd their Tents on the *North* Shore of the Island, but a little more to the *West*, to be out of the Danger of the Savages, who always landed on the *East* Parts of the Island.

Here they built them two Huts, one to lodge in, and the other to lay up their Magazines and Stores in, and the *Spaniards* having given them some Corn for Seed, and especially some of the Peas which I had left them, they dug, and planted, and enclosed, after the Pattern I had set for them all, and began to live pretty well; their first Crop of Corn was on the Ground; and tho' it was but a little Bit of Land which they had dug up at first, having had but a little Time, yet it was enough to relieve them, and find them with Bread and other Eatables; and one of the Fellows being the Cook's Mate of the Ship, was very ready at making Soup, Puddings, and such other Preparations, as the Rice, and the Milk, and such little Flesh as they got, furnish'd him to do.

They were going on in this little thriving Poſture, when the three unnatural Rogues, their own Country-men too, in meer Humour, and to insult them, came and bully'd them, and told them, the Island was theirs, that the Governor, meaning me, had given them Possession of it, and no Body else had any Right to it, and damn 'em, they should build no Houses upon their Ground, unless they would pay them Rent for them.

The two Men thought they had jeſted at firſt, ask'd them to come in and sit down, and see what fine Houses they were that they had built, and tell them what Rent they demanded, and one of them merrily told them, if they were Ground-Landlords, he hoped, if they built Tenements upon their Land, and made Improvements, they would, according to the Cuſtom of Landlords, grant them a long Lease, and bid them go fetch a Scrivener to draw the Writings. One of the three damning and raging told them, they should see they were not in Jeſt, and going to a little Place at a Diſtance, where the honeſt Men had made a Fire to dress their Victuals, he takes a Fire-brand, and claps it to the Out-side of their Hut, and very fairly set it on Fire, and it would have been all burnt down in a few Minutes, if one of the two had not run to the Fellow, thruſt him away, and trod the Fire out with his Feet, and that not without some Difficulty too.

The Fellow was in such a Rage at the honeſt Man's thruſting him away, that he return'd upon him with a Pole he had in his Hand, and had not the Man avoided the Blow very nimbly, and run into the Hut, he had ended his Days at once; his Comrade seeing the Danger they were both in, run in after him, and immediately they came both out with their Muskets, and the Man that was first struck at with the Pole, knock'd the Fellow down, that begun the Quarrel, with the Stock of his Musket, and that before the other two could come to help him, and then seeing the rest come at them, they stood together, and presenting the other Ends of their Pieces to them, bad them stand off.

The other had Fire-Arms with them too, but one of the two honest Men, bolder than his Comrade, and made desperate by his Danger, told them, if they offer'd to move Hand or Foot they were dead Men, and boldly commanded them to lay down their Amrs. They did not indeed lay down their Arms, but seeing him so resolute, it brought them to a Parley, and they consented to take their wounded Man with them, and be gone; and indeed it seems the Fellow was wounded sufficiently with the Blow; however, they were much in the wrong, since they had the Advantage, that they did not disarm them effectually, as they might have done, and have gone immediately to the *Spaniards*, and given them an Account how the Rogues had treated them; for the three Villains studied nothing but Revenge, and every Day gave them some Intimation that they did so.

But not to crowd this Part with an Account of the lesser Part of their Rogueries, such as treading down their Corn, shooting three young Kids, and a She-Goat, which the poor Men had got to breed up tame for their Store; and, in a word, plaguing them Night and Day in this Manner, it forced the two Men to such a Desperation, that they resolv'd to fight them all three the first Time they had a fair Opportunity; in Order to this, they resolv'd to go to the Castle, as they call'd it, that was my old Dwelling, where the three Rogues and the *Spaniards* all liv'd together, at that Time intending to have a fair Battle, and the *Spaniards* should stand by to see fair Play; so they got up in the Morning before Day, and came to the Place, and call'd the *English* Men by their Names, telling a *Spaniard*, that answer'd, that they wanted to speak with them.

It happen'd, that the Day before two of the *Spaniards* having been in the Woods, had seen one of the two *English* Men, who, for Distinction, I call the *Honest Men*, and he had made a sad Complaint to the *Spaniards*, of the barbarous Usage they had met with from their three Countrymen, and how they had ruin'd their Plantation, and destroy'd their Corn, that they had labour'd so hard to bring forward, and kill'd the Milch-Goat and their three Kids, which was all they had provided for their Sustenance, and that if he and his Friends, meaning the *Spaniards*, did not assist them again, they should be starved. When the *Spaniards* came home at Night, and they were all at Supper, he took the Freedom to reprove the three *English* Men, tho' in very gentle and mannerly Terms, and ask'd them, How they could be so cruel, they being harmless inoffensive Fellows, and that they were only putting themselves in a way to subsist by their Labour, and that it had cost them a great deal of Pains to bring things to such Perfection as they had?

One of the *English* Men return'd very briskly, what had they to do there? That they came on Shore without Leave, and they should not Plant or Build upon the Island, it was none of their Ground. Why, says the *Spaniard* very calmly, Seignior Inglese, *they must not starve?* The *English* Man reply'd like a true rough-hewn Tarpaulin, they might Starve and be Damn'd, they should not Plant nor Build. But what must they do then, Seignior, said the

Spaniard? Another of the Brutes return'd, do! D....m'em, they should be Servants, and work for them. But how can you expect that of them, says the *Spaniard*, they are not bought with your Money; you have no Right to make them Servants. The *English* Man answer'd, the Island was theirs, the Governour had given it to them, and no Man had any thing to do there but themselves; and with that swore by his Maker, that they would go and burn all their new Huts, they should build none upon their Land.

Why, Seignior, says the *Spaniard*, by the same Rule we must be your Servants too? Ay, says the bold Dog, and so you shall too, before we have done with you, mixing two or three G—d Damme's in the proper Intervals of his Speech; the *Spaniard* only smil'd at that, and made him no Answer: However, this little Discourse had heated them, and starting up, one says to the other, I think it was he they call'd *Will. Atkins*, Come *Jack*, let us go and have t'other Brush with them; we'll demolish their Castle, I'll warrant you, they shall plant no Colony in our Dominions.

Upon this, they went all Trooping away, with every Man a Gun, a Pistol, and a Sword, and mutter'd some insolent Things among themselves of what they would do to the *Spaniards* too, when Opportunity offer'd, but the *Spaniards* it seems did not so perfectly understand them, as to know all the Particulars, only, that in general, they threatned them hard for taking the two *English* Mens Part.

Whether they went, or how they bestow'd their Time that Evening, the *Spaniards* said, they did not know; but it seems they wandred about the Country, Part of the Night, and then lying down in the Place which I used to call my Bower, they were weary, and over-slept themselves. The Case was this, they had resolv'd to stay till Midnight, and so to take the two poor Men when they were asleep, and as they acknowledg'd afterwards, intended to set Fire to their Huts while they were in them, and either burn them in them, or murder them as they came out, and as Malice seldom sleeps very sound, it was very strange they should not have been kept waking.

However, as the two Men had also a Design upon them, as I have said, tho' a much fairer one than that of Burning and Murthering, it happen'd, and very luckily for them all, that they were up and gone abroad, before the bloody-minded Rogues came to their Huts.

When they came there and found the Men gone, *Atkins*, who it seems was the forwardest Man, call'd out to his Comrades, ha *Jack*, here's the Nest, but D....n 'em the Birds are flown; they mused a while to think what should be the Occasion of their being gone abroad so soon, and suggested presently that the *Spaniards* had given them Notice of it, and with that they shook Hands, and swore to one another that they would be reveng'd of the *Spaniards*. As soon as they had made this bloody Bargain, they fell to work with the poor Mens Habitation, they did not set Fire indeed to any thing, but they pull'd down both their little Houses, and pull'd them so Limb from Limb, that they left not the least Stick standing, or scarce any Sign on the Ground where they stood; they tore all their little collected Houshold Stuff in Pieces, and threw every Thing about in such a manner, that the poor Men afterwards found some of their Things a Mile off of their Habitation.

When they had done this, they pull'd up all the young Trees the poor Men had planted, pull'd up an Enclosure they had made to secure their Cattle and their Corn; and in a word, sack'd and plunder'd every thing, as compleatly as a Hoord of *Tartars* would have done.

The two Men were at this Juncture gone to find them out, and had resolved to fight them wherever they had been, tho' they were but two to three: So that had they met, there certainly would have been Blood shed among them, for they were all very stout resolute Fellows, to give them their due.

But Providence took more Care to keep them assunder, than they themselves could do to meet; for, as if they had dogg'd one another, when the three were gone thither, the two were here; and afterwards when the two went back to find them, the three were come to the old Habitation again; we shall see their differing Conduct presently. When the three came back like furious Creatures flush'd with the Rage which the Work they had been about had put them into, they came up to the *Spaniards*, and told them what they had done, by way of Scoff and Bravado; and one of them stepping up to one of the *Spaniards*, as if they had been a Couple of Boys at Play, takes hold of his Hat, as it was upon his Head, and giving it a Twirl about, fleering in his Face, says he to him, *And you*, Seignior, Jack Spaniard, *shall have the same Sauce, if you do not mend your Manners:* The *Spaniard*, who tho' a quiet civil Man, was as brave as a Man could be desir'd to be, and withal a strong well-made Man, look'd steadily at him for a good while, and then having no Weapon in his Hand, stept gravely up to him, and with one Blow of his Fist knock'd him down, as an Ox is fell'd with a Pole-Axe; at which one of the Rogues, insolent as the first, fir'd his Pistol at the *Spaniard* immediately; he miss'd his Body indeed, for the Bullets went thro' his Hair, but one of them touch'd the tip of his Ear, and he bled pretty much. The Blood made the *Spaniard* believe, he was more hurt than he really was, and that put him into some Heat, for before, he acted all in a perfect Calm; but now resolving to go thro' with his Work, he stoop'd to take the Fellow's Musket who he had knock'd down, and was just going to shoot the Man, and had fir'd at him, when the rest of the *Spaniards* being in the Cave came out, and calling to him not to shoot, they stept in, secur'd the other two, and took their Arms from them.

When they were thus disarm'd, and found they had made all the *Spaniards* their Enemies, as well as their own Countrymen, they began to cool, and giving the *Spaniards* better Words, would have had their Arms again; but the *Spaniards* considering the Feud that was between them and the other two *English* Men, and that it would be the best Method they could take to keep them from one another, told them, they would do them no harm, and if they would live peaceably, they would be very willing to assist and sociate with them, as they did before; but that they could not think of giving them their Arms again, while they appear'd so resolv'd to do Mischief with them to their own Countrymen, and had even threatned them all, to make them their Servants.

The Rogues were now no more capable to hear Reason, than to act Reason, and being refus'd their Arms, they went raving away and raging like mad Men, threatning what they would do, tho' they had no Fire-Arms. But the *Spaniards* despising their Threatning, told them they should take Care how they offer'd any Injury to their Plantation or Cattle, for if they did, they would shoot them as they would do ravenous Beasts, wherever they found them; and if they fell into their Hands alive, they should certainly be hang'd. However, this was far from cooling them, but away they went raging and swearing like Furies of Hell. As soon as they were gone, came back the two Men in Passion and Rage enough also, tho' of another Kind; for having been at their Plantation, and finding it all demolish'd and deſtroy'd, as above, it will easily be suppos'd they had Provocation enough; they could scarce have Room to tell their Tale, the *Spaniards* were so eager to tell them theirs; and it was ſtrange enough to find three Men thus bully nineteen, and receive no Punishment at all.

The *Spaniards* indeed despised them, and especially having thus disarm'd them, made light of all their Threatnings; but the two *English* Men resolv'd to have their Remedy againſt them, what Pain soever it coſt to find them out.

But the *Spaniards* interpos'd here too, and told them, that as they had disarm'd them, they could not consent that they (the Two) should pursue them with Fire-Arms and perhaps kill them; but said the grave *Spaniard*, who was their Governour, we will endeavour to make them do you Juſtice if you will leave it to us, for as there is no doubt but they will come to us again when their Passion is over, being not able to subsiſt without our Assiſtance, we promise you to make no Peace with them, without having a full Satisfaction for you; upon this Condition we hope you will promise to use no Violence with them, other than in your own Defence.

The two *English* Men yielded to this very awkardly, and with great Reluctance; but the *Spaniards* proteſted, they did it only to keep them from Bloodshed, and to make all easy at laſt; for said they, we are not so many of us, here is Room enough for us all, and it is great pity we should not be all good Friends; at length they did consent, and waited for the Issue of the Thing, living for some Days with the *Spaniards*, for their own Habitation was deſtroyed.

In about five Days Time the three Vagrants, tir'd with Wandring, and almoſt ſtarv'd with Hunger, having chiefly liv'd on Turtles Eggs all that while, came back to the Grove, and finding my *Spaniard*, who, as I have said, was the Governour, and two more with him walking by the Side of the Creek; they came up in a very submissive humble Manner, and begg'd to be receiv'd again into the Family. The *Spaniards* used them civilly, but told them, they had acted so unnaturally by their Countrymen, and so very grossly by them (the *Spaniards*) that they could not come to any Conclusion without consulting the two *English* Men and the reſt; but however, they would go to them and discourse about it, and they should know in half an Hour. It may be guess'd, that they were very hard put to it, for it seems, as they were to wait this half Hour for an Answer, they begg'd they would send them out some Bread in the mean Time, which he did, and sent them at the same Time a large Piece of Goats Flesh, and a broil'd Parrot, which they eat very heartily, for they were hungry enough.

After half an Hour's Consultation they were call'd in, and a long Debate had among them, their two Countrymen charging them with the Ruin of all their Labour, and a Design to murther them; all which they own'd before, and therefore could not deny now; upon the whole, the *Spaniard* acted the Moderator between them, and as they had oblig'd the two *English* Men not to hurt the three while they were naked and unarm'd, so they now oblig'd the three to go and build their Fellows two Huts, one of the same, and the other of larger Dimensions, than they were before; to fence their Ground again where they had pull'd up the Fences, plant Trees in the Room of those pull'd up, dig up the Land again for planting Corn, where they had spoil'd it; and in a Word, to restore every Thing in the same State as they found it, as near as they could, for entirely it could not be, the Season for the Corn, and the Growth of the Trees, and Hedges, not being possible to be recovered.

Well, they submitted to all this, and as they had Plenty of Provisions given them all the while, they grew very orderly, and the whole Society began to live pleasantly and agreeably together, only that these three Fellows could never be persuaded to work, I mean for themselves, except now and then a little, just as they pleased; however, the *Spaniards* told them plainly, that if they would but live sociably and friendly together, and study in the whole the Good of the Plantation, they would be content to work for them, and let them walk about and be as idle as they pleas'd; and thus having liv'd pretty well together for a Month or two, the *Spaniards* gave them Arms again, and gave them Liberty to go abroad with them as before.

It was not above a Week after they had these Arms, and went abroad, but the ungrateful Creatures began to be as insolent and troublesome as before; but however, an Accident happening presently upon this, which endanger'd the Safety of them all, they were oblig'd to lay by all private Resentments, and look to the Preservation of their Lives.

It happen'd one Night, that the *Spaniard* Governour, as I call him, that is to say, the *Spaniard*, whose Life I had sav'd, who was now the Captain, or Leader, or Governour of the rest, found himself very uneasy in the Night, and could by no Means get any Sleep; he was perfectly well in

Body, as he told me the Story, only found his Thoughts tumultuous, his Mind run upon Men fighting, and killing of one another, but was broad awake, and could not by any Means get any Sleep; in short, he lay a great while, but growing more and more uneasy, he resolv'd to rise: As they lay, being so many of them, upon Goats-skins, laid thick upon such Couches and Pads, as they made for themselves, not in Hammocks and Ship-Beds, as I did, who was but one, so they had little to do, when they were willing to rise, but to get up upon their Feet, and perhaps put on a Coat, such as it was, and their Pumps, and they were ready for going any Way that their Thoughts guided them.

Being thus gotten up, he look'd out, but being dark, he could see little or nothing, and besides the Trees which I had planted, as in my former Account is described, and which were now grown tall intercepted his Sight, so that he could only look up, and see that it was a clear Star-light Night, and hearing no Noise, he return'd and laid him down again; but it was all one, he could not sleep, nor could he compose himself to any Thing like Rest, but his Thoughts were to the last Degree uneasy, and yet he knew not for what.

Having made some Noise with rising and walking about, going out and coming in, another of them wak'd, and calling, ask'd, who it was that was up? The Governour told him, how it had been with him. Say you so, says the other *Spaniard*, such Things are not to be slighted, I assure you; there is certainly some Mischief working, says he, near us, and presently he asked him, where are the *English* Men? They are all in their Huts, says he, safe enough. It seems, the *Spaniards* had kept Possession of the main Apartment, and had made a Place where the three *English* Men, since their laſt Mutiny always quarter'd by themselves, and could not come at the reſt. Well, says the *Spaniard*, there is something in it, I am persuaded from my own Experience; I am satisfied our Spirits embodied have a Converse with, and receive Intelligence from the Spirits unembodied and inhabiting the invisible World, and this friendly Notice is given for our Advantage, if we know how to make Use of it. Come, says he, let us go out and look abroad, and if we find nothing at all in it to juſtify the Trouble, I'll tell you a Story to the Purpose, that shall convince you of the Juſtice of my proposing it.

In a Word, they went out to go up to the Top of the Hill, where I us'd to go, but they being ſtrong and in good Company, not alone, as I was, us'd none of my Cautions, to go up by the Ladder, and then pulling it up after them, to go up a second Stage to the Top, but were going round thro' the Grove unconcern'd and unwary, when they were surpriz'd with seeing a Light, as of Fire, a very little Way off from them, and hearing the Voices of Men, not of one, or two, but of a great Number.

In all the Discoveries I had made of the Savages landing on the Island, it was my conſtant Care to prevent them making the leaſt Discovery of there being any Inhabitant upon the Place; and when by any Occasion they came to know it, they felt it so effeɛtually, that they that got away, were scarce able to give any Account of it, for we disappear'd as soon as possible, nor did ever any that had seen me, escape to tell any one else, except it was the three Savages in our laſt Encounter, who jump'd into the Boat, of whom I mention'd, that I was afraid they should go Home and bring more Help.

Whether it was the Consequence of the Escape of those

Men, that so great a Number came now together, or whether they came ignorantly and by Accident on their usual bloody Errand, they could not it seems underſtand; but whatever it was, it had been their Business, either to have conceal'd themselves, as not to have seen them at all, much less to have let the Savages have seen that there were any Inhabitants in the Place, or to have fallen upon them so effectually, as that not a Man of them should have escap'd, which could only have been, by getting in between them and their Boats; but this Presence of Mind was wanting to them, which was the Ruin of their Tranquillity for a great while.

We need not doubt, but that the Governour and the Man with him, surpriz'd with this Sight, run back immediately, and rais'd their Fellows, giving them an Account of the imminent Danger they were all in; and they again as readily took the Alarm, but it was impossible to persuade them to ſtay close within where they were, but that they muſt run all out to see how Things ſtood.

While it was dark indeed, they were well enough, and they had Opportunity enough for some Hours to view them by the Light of three Fires they had made at a Distance from one another; what they were doing they knew not, and what to do themselves they knew not. For, firſt, the Enemy were too many; and secondly, they did not keep together, but were divided into several Parties, and were on Shore in several Places.

The *Spaniards* were in no small Conſternation at this Sight, and as they found that the Fellows ran ſtraggling all over the Shore, they made no doubt, but firſt or laſt, some of them would chop in upon their Habitation, or upon some other Place, where they would see the Token of Inhabitants, and they were in great Perplexity also for fear of their Flock of Goats, which would have been little less than starving them, if they should have been destroy'd; so the first Thing they resolv'd upon, was to dispatch three Men away before it was light, *viz.* two *Spaniards* and one *Englishman*, to drive all the Goats away to the great Valley where the Cave was, and if Need were, to drive them into the very Cave itself.

Could they have seen the Savages altogether in one Body, and at any Distance from their Canoes, they resolv'd, if they had been an hundred of them, to have attack'd them; but that could not be obtain'd, for they were some of them two Miles off from the other, and, as it appear'd afterwards, were of two different Nations.

After having mused a great while on the Course they should take, and beaten their Brains in considering their present Circumstances, they resolv'd at last, while it was dark, to send the old Savage, *Friday's* Father, out as a Spy, to learn, if possible, something concerning them, what they came for, and what they intended to do; the old Man readily undertook it, and stripping himself quite naked, as most of the Savages were, away he went: After he had been gone an Hour or two, he brings Word, that he had been among them undiscover'd, that he found they were two Parties, and of two several Nations who had War with one another, and had had a great Battle in their own Country, and that both Sides having had several Prisoners taken in the Fight, they were by meer Chance landed all in the same Island, for the devouring their Prisoners, and making merry; but their coming so by Chance to the same Place had spoil'd all their Mirth; that they were in a great Rage at one another, and that they were so near, that he believ'd they would fight again as soon as Daylight began to appear; but he did not perceive that they had any Notion of any Body's being on the Island but themselves. He had hardly made an End of telling his Story, when they could perceive, by the unusual Noise they made, that the two little Armies were engag'd in a bloody Fight.

Friday's Father used all the Arguments he could to persuade our People to lie close, and not be seen; he told them their Safety consisted in it, and that they had nothing to do but lie still, and the Savages would kill one another to their Hands, and then the rest would go away; and it was so to a Tittle. But it was impossible to prevail, especially upon the *Englishmen*, their Curiosity was so importunate upon their Prudentials, that they must run out and see the Battle: However, they used some Caution too, (*viz.*) they did not go openly, just by their own Dwelling, but went farther into the Woods, and plac'd themselves to Advantage, where they might securely see them manage the Fight, and, as they thought, not to be seen by them; but it seems the Savages did see them, as we shall find hereafter.

The Battle was very fierce, and if I might believe the *Englishmen*, one of them said, he could perceive, that some of them were Men of great Bravery, of invincible Spirits, and of great Policy in guiding the Fight. The Battle, they said, held two Hours, before they could guess which Party would be beaten; but then that Party which was nearest our Peoples Habitation began to appear weakest, and after some Time more, some of them began to fly; and this put our Men again into a great Consternation, least any of those that fled should run into the Grove before their Dwelling, for Shelter, and thereby involuntarily discover the Place; and that by Consequence the Pursuers should do the like in Search for them. Upon this they resolv'd that they would ſtand arm'd within the Wall, and whoever came into the Grove, they should sally out over the Wall and kill them; so that, if possible, not one should return to give an Account of it; they order'd also, that it should be done with their Swords, or by knocking them down with the Stock of the Musket, but not by shooting them, for fear of the Noise.

As they expected, it fell out; three of the routed Army fled for Life, and, crossing the Creek, ran directly into the Place, not in the leaſt knowing whether they went, but running as into a thick Wood for Shelter; the Scout they kept to look Abroad, gave Notice of this within, with this Addition, to our Mens great Satisfaction (*viz.*) That the Conquerors had not pursued them, or seen which Way they were gone; upon this, the *Spaniard* Governour, a Man of Humanity, would not suffer them to kill the three Fugitives, but sending three Men out by the Top of the Hill, order'd them to go round and come in behind them, surprize and take them Prisoners, which was done; the Residue of the conquer'd People fled to their Canoes, and got off to Sea; the Victors retir'd, and made no Pursuit or very little, but drawing themselves into a Body together, gave two great skreaming Shouts, which they suppos'd was by way of Triumph, and so the Fight ended: And the same Day, about three a Clock in the Afternoon, they also march'd to their Canoes, and thus the *Spaniards* had their Island again free to themselves, their Fright was over, and they saw no Savages in several Years after.

After they were all gone, the *Spaniards* came out of their Den, and viewing the Field of Battle, they found about two and thirty dead Men upon the Spot; some were kill'd with great long Arrows, some of which were found ſticking in their Bodies; but moſt of them were kill'd with their great wooden Swords, sixteen or seventeen of which they found in the Field of Battle, and as many Bows, with a great many Arrows: These Swords were ſtrange great unweildy Things, and they muſt be very ſtrong Men that used them: Moſt of those Men that were kill'd with them, had their Heads mash'd to Pieces, as we may say, or as we call it in *English*, their Brains knock'd out, and several their Arms and Legs broken; so that 'tis evident they fight with inexpressible Rage and Fury. We found not one wounded Man that was not ſtone dead; for either they ſtay by their Enemy till they have quite kill'd him, or they carry all the wounded Men, that are not quite dead, away with them.

This Deliverance tam'd our *English* Men for a great while; the Sight had fill'd them with Horror, and the Consequences appear'd terrible to the laſt Degree, even to them, if ever they should fall into the Hands of those Creatures, who would not only kill them as Enemies, but kill them for Food, as we kill our Cattle. And they profess'd to me, that the Thoughts of being eaten up like Beef or Mutton, tho' it was suppos'd it was not to be till they were dead, had something in it so horrible, that it nauseated their very Stomachs, made them sick when they thought of it, and fill'd their Minds with such unusual Terror, that they were not themselves for some Weeks after.

This, as I said, tam'd even the three *English* Brutes I have been speaking of; and for a great while after they were very tractable, and went about the common Business of their whole Society well enough; planted, sow'd, reap'd, and began to be all naturaliz'd to the Country.

But sometime after this, they fell all into such Measures which brought them into a great deal of Trouble.

They had taken three Prisoners, as I had observ'd, and these three being lusty stout young Fellows, they made them Servants, and taught them to work for them, and as Slaves they did well enough; but they did not take their Measures with them as I did by my Man *Friday*, *viz.* to begin with them upon the Principle of having sav'd their Lives, and then instruct them in the rational Principles of Life, much less of Religion, civilizing and reducing them by kind Usage and affectionate Arguings; but as they gave them their Food every Day, so they gave them their Work too, and kept them fully employ'd in Drudgery enough; but they fail'd in this, by it, that they never had them to assist them and fight for them, as I had my Man *Friday*, who was as true to me as the very Flesh upon my Bones.

But to come to the Family Part, being all now good Friends, for common Danger, as I said above, had effectually reconcil'd them, they began to consider their general Circumstances; and the first Thing that came under their Consideration was, Whether, seeing the Savages particularly haunted that Side of the Island, and that there were more remote and retir'd Parts of it equally adapted to their Way of Living, and manifestly to their Advantage, they should not rather remove their Habitation, and plant in some more proper Place for their Safety, and especially for the Security of their Cattle and Corn?

Upon this, after long Debate, it was concluded, That they would not remove their Habitation; because, that some Time or other, they thought they might hear from their Governor again, meaning me; and if I should send any one to seek them, I should be to sure direct them to that Side, where, if they should find the Place demolish'd, they would conclude the Savages had kill'd us all, and we were gone, and so our Supply would go too.

But as to their Corn and Cattle, they agreed to remove them into the Valley where my Cave was, where the Land was as proper for both, and where indeed there was Land enough: However, upon second Thought, they alter'd one Part of that Resolution too, and resolv'd only to remove Part of their Cattle thither, and plant Part of their Corn there; and so if one Part was destroy'd, the other might be sav'd: And one Part of Prudence they used, which it was very well they did, *viz.* That they never trusted those three Savages, which they had Prisoners, with knowing any Thing of the Plantation they had made in that Valley, or of any Cattle they had there; much less of the Cave there, which they kept, in Case of Necessity, as a safe Retreat, and whither they carry'd also the two Barrels of Powder, which I had sent them at my coming away.

But however they resolv'd not to change their Habitation, yet they agreed, that as I had carefully cover'd it first with a Wall or Fortification, and then with a Grove of Trees; so, seeing their Safety consisted entirely in their being conceal'd, of which they were now fully convinc'd, they set to work to cover and conceal the Place yet more effectually than before: To this Purpose, as I had planted Trees, (or rather thrust in Stakes, which in Time all grew up to be Trees) for some good Distance before the Entrance into my Apartment, they went on in the same Manner, and fill'd up the rest of that whole Space of Ground, from the Trees I had set, quite down to the Side of the Creek, where, as I said, I landed my Floats, and even into the very Ouze where the Tide flow'd, not so much as leaving any Place to land, or any Sign that there had been any Landing thereabout: These Stakes also, being of a Wood very forward to grow, as I have noted formerly, they took Care to have generally very much larger and taller than those which I had planted; and as they grew apace, so they planted them so very thick and close together, that when they had been three or four Years grown, there was no piercing with the Eye any considerable Way into the Plantation. And as for that Part which I had planted, the Trees were grown as thick as a Man's Thigh; and among them they placed so many other short ones, and so thick, that, in a Word, it stood like a Pallisado, a quarter of a Mile thick, and it was next to impossible to penetrate it, but with a little Army to cut it all down; for a little Dog could hardly get between the Trees, they stood so close.

But this was not all; for they did the same by all the Ground to the right Hand, and to the Left, and round even to the Top of the Hill; leaving no Way, not so much as for themselves to come out, but by the Ladder placed up to the Side of the Hill, and then lifted up, and placed again from the first Stage up to the Top; which Ladder, when it was taken down, nothing but what had Wings or Witchcraft to assist it, could come at them.

This was excellently well contriv'd; nor was it less than what they afterwards found Occasion for; which serv'd to convince me, that as human Prudence has the Authority of Providence to justify it, so it has, doubtless, the Direction of Providence to set it to Work; and would we listen carefully to the Voice of it, I am fully persuaded we might prevent many of the Disasters, which our Lives are now, by our own Negligence, subjected to. But this by the Way.

I return to the Story. They liv'd two Years after this in perfect Retirement, and had no more Visits from the Savages: They had indeed an Alarm given them one Morning, which put them into a great Consternation; for some of the *Spaniards* being out early one Morning on the West Side, or rather the End of the Island, which by the Way was that End where I never went, for fear of being discover'd, they were surpriz'd with seeing above twenty Canoes of *Indians* just coming on Shore.

They made the best of their Way Home, in Hurry enough; and, giving the Alarm to their Comrades, they kept close all that Day and the next, going out only at Night, to make Observation: But they had the good Luck to be mistaken; for, wherever the Savages went, they did not land at that Time on the Island, but pursued some other Design.

And now they had another Broil with the three *Englishmen*; one of which, a most turbulent Fellow, being in a Rage at one of the three Slaves, which I mention'd they had taken, because the Fellow had not done something right which he bid him do, and seem'd a little untractable in his shewing him, drew a Hatchet out of a Frog-Belt, in which he wore it by his Side, and fell upon the poor Savage, not to correct him, but to kill him. One of the *Spaniards*, who was by, seeing him give the Fellow a barbarous Cut with the Hatchet, which he aimed at his Head, but struck into his Shoulder, so that he thought he had cut the poor Creature's Arm off, ran to him, and entreating him not to murder the poor Man, clapt in between him and the Savage, to prevent the Mischief.

The Fellow being enrag'd the more at this, struck at the *Spaniard* with his Hatchet, and swore he would serve him as he intended to serve the Savage; which the *Spani-*

ard perceiving, avoided the Blow; and with a Shovel which he had in his Hand, (for they were all working in the Field about their Corn-Land) knock'd the Brute down: Another of the *Englishmen* running at the same Time to help his Comrade, knock'd the *Spaniard* down; and then two *Spaniards* more came in to help their Man, and a third *Englishman* fell in upon them. They had none of them any Fire-Arms, or any other Weapons but Hatchets and other Tools, except this third *Englishman*; he had one of my old rusty Cutlasses, with which he made at the two last *Spaniards*, and wounded them both. This Fray set the whole Family in an Uproar, and more help coming in, they took the three *Englishmen* Prisoners. The next Question was, What should be done with them, they had been so often mutinous, and were so furious, so desperate, and so idle withal, that they knew not what Course to take with them; for they were mischievous to the highest Degree, and valued not what Hurt they did to any man; so that, in short, it was not safe to live with them.

The *Spaniard*, who was Governor, told them in so many Words, That if they had been of his own Country, he would have hang'd them; for all Laws and all Governours were to preserve Society; and those who were dangerous to the Society, ought to be expell'd out of it; but as they were *Englishmen*, and that it was to the generous Kindness of an *Englishman* that they all ow'd their Preservation and Deliverance, he would use them with all possible Lenity, and would leave them to the Judgment of the other two *Englishmen*, who were their Countrymen.

One of the two honest *Englishmen* stood up, and said, they desir'd it might not be left to them; for, says he, I am sure we ought to sentence them to the Gallows; and with that he gives an Account how *Will. Atkins*, one of the three, had proposed to have all the five *Englishmen* join together, and murder all the *Spaniards* when they were in their Sleep.

When the *Spanish* Governor heard this, he calls to *William Atkins*, How, Seignior *Atkins*, says he, would you murder us all? What have you to say to that? That harden'd Villain was so far from denying it, that he said it was true, and G....d d....m him they would do it ſtill before they had done with them. Well, but Seignior *Atkins*, says the *Spaniard*, What have we done to you, that you will kill us? And what would you get by killing us? And what muſt we do to prevent you killing us? Muſt we kill you, or you will kill us? Why will you put us to the Necessity of this, Seignior *Atkins*, says the *Spaniard* very calmly and smiling?

Seignior *Atkins* was in such a Rage at the *Spaniard's* making a Jeſt of it, that had he not been held by three Men, and withal had no Weapons with him, it was thought he would have attempted to have kill'd the *Spaniard* in the Middle of all the Company.

This hair-brain'd Carriage oblig'd them to consider seriously what was to be done. The two *Englishmen* and the *Spaniard* who sav'd the poor Savage, was of the Opinion, they should hang one of the three for an Example to the reſt, and that, particularly, it should be he that had twice attempted to commit Murder with his Hatchet; and indeed there was some Reason to believe he had done it, for the poor Savage was in such a miserable Condition with the Wound he had receiv'd, that it was thought he could not live.

But the Governor *Spaniard* ſtill said No, it was an *Englishman* that had sav'd all their Lives, and he would never consent to put an *Englishman* to Death, tho' he had murder'd half of them, nay, he said, if he had been kill'd himself by an *Englishman*, and had time left to speak, it should be, that they should pardon him.

This was so positively insisted on by the Governor *Spaniard*, that there was no gainsaying it; and as merciful Councils are most apt to prevail where they are so earnestly press'd, so they all came into it; but then it was to be consider'd, what should be done to keep them from doing the Mischief they design'd; for all agreed, Governor and all, that Means were to be used for preserving the Society from Danger; after a long Debate it was agreed, First, That they should be disarm'd, and not permitted to have either Gun, or Powder, or Shot, or Sword, or any Weapon, and should be turn'd out of the Society, and left to live where they would, and how they would, by themselves; but that none of the rest, either *Spaniards* or *English*, should converse with them, speak with them, or have any Thing to do with them; that they should be forbid to come within a certain Distance of the Place where the rest dwelt; and that if they offer'd to commit any Disorder, so as to spoil, burn, kill, or destroy any of the Corn, Plantings, Buildings, Fences, or Cattle belonging to the Society, they should dye without Mercy, and they would shoot them wherever they could find them.

The Governor, a Man of great Humanity, musing upon the Sentence, consider'd a little upon it, and turning to the two honest *Englishmen* said, Hold, you must reflect, that it will be long e'er they can raise Corn and Cattle of their own, and they must not starve: We must therefore allow them Provisions, so he caus'd to be added, That they should have a Proportion of Corn given them to last them eight Months, and for Seed to sow, by which Time they might be suppos'd to raise some of their own;

that they should have six Milch-Goats, four He-Goats, and six Kids given them, as well for present Subsistence, as for a Store; and that they should have Tools given them for their Work in the Fields; such as, six Hatchets, an Axe, a Saw, and the like: But they should have none of these Tools, or Provisions, unless they would swear solemnly, that they would not hurt or injure any of the *Spaniards* with them, or of their Fellow *Englishmen*.

Thus they dismiss'd them the Society, and turn'd them out to shift for themselves. They went away sullen and refractory, as neither contented to go away, or to stay; but, as there was no Remedy, they went, pretending, to go and choose a Place where they would settle themselves to plant and live by themselves, and some Provision[s] were given them, but no Weapons.

About four or five Days after, they came again for some Victuals, and gave the Governour an Account where they had pitch'd their Tents, and mark'd themselves out an Habitation and Plantation; and it was a very convenient Place indeed, on the remotest Part of the Island, N.E. much about the Place where I landed in my first Voyage, when I was driven out to Sea, the Lord knows whether, in my Attempt to surround the Island.

Here they built themselves two handsome Huts, and contriv'd them, in a Manner, like my first Habitation, being close under the Side of a Hill, having some Trees growing already on three Sides of it, so that by planting others it would be very easily cover'd from the Sight, unless narrowly search'd for; they desir'd some dry'd Goats-skins for Beds and Covering, which were given them; and upon giving their Words, that they would not disturb the rest, or injure any of their Plantations, they gave them Hatchets, and what other Tools they could spare, some Peas, Barley, and Rice, for sowing, and, in a Word, any thing they wanted, but Arms and Ammunition.

They liv'd in this separate Condition about six Months, and had gotten in their first Harvest, tho' the Quantity was but small, the Parcel of Land they had planted being but little; for indeed, having all their Plantation to form, they had a great deal of Work upon their Hands; and when they came to make Boards, and Pots, and such Things, they were quite out of their Element, and could make nothing of it; and when the rainy Season came on, for want of a Cave in the Earth, they could not keep their Grain dry, and it was in great Danger of spoiling: And this humbled them much; so they came and begg'd the *Spaniards* to help them, which they very readily did, and in four Days work'd a great Hole in the Side of the Hill for them, big enough to secure their Corn, and other Things from the Rain; but it was but a poor Place, at best, compar'd to mine; and especially as mine was then, for the *Spaniards* had greatly enlarg'd it, and made several new Apartments in it.

About three Quarters of a Year after this Separation, a new Frolick took these Rogues, which, together with the former Villany they had committed, brought Mischief enough upon them, and had very near been the Ruin of the whole Colony: The three new Sociates began, it seems to be weary of the laborious Life they led, and that without Hope of bettering their Circumstances; and a Whim took them, that they would make a Voyage to the Continent from whence the Savages came, and would try if they could not seize upon some Prisoners among the Natives there, and bring them Home, so to make them do the laborious Part of their Work for them.

The Project was not so preposterous, if they had gone no farther; but they did nothing, and propos'd nothing, but had either Mischief in the Design, or Mischief in the Event: And if I may give my Opinion, they seem'd to be under a Blast from Heaven; for if we will not allow a visible Curse to pursue visible Crimes, how shall we reconcile the Events of Things with the Divine Justice? It was certainly an apparent Vengeance on their Crime of Mutiny and Piracy, that brought them to the State they were in; and as they shew'd not the least Remorse for the Crime, but added new Villanies to it, such as, particularly, the Piece of monstrous Cruelty of wounding a poor Slave, because he did not, or perhaps could not, understand to do what he was directed; and to wound him in such a Manner, as, no Question, made him a Cripple all his Life; and in a Place where no Surgeon or Medicine could be had for his Cure; and what was still worse, the murderous Intent, or, to do Justice to the Crime, the intentional Murder, for such, to be sure it was, as was afterwards the form'd Design they all laid, to murder the *Spaniards* in cold Blood, and in their Sleep.

But I leave observing, and return to the Story: The three Fellows comes down to the *Spaniards* one Morning, and in very humble Terms desir'd to be admitted to speak with them: The *Spaniards* very readily heard what they had to say, which was this, That they were tir'd of living in the Manner they did; that they were not handy enough to make the Necessaries they wanted; and that having no Help, they found they should be starv'd: But if the *Spaniards* would give them Leave to take one of the Canoes which they came over in, and give them Arms and Ammunition, proportion'd for their Defence, they would go over to the Main, and seek their Fortune, and so deliver them from the Trouble of supplying them with any other Provisions.

The *Spaniards* were glad enough to be rid of them, but yet very honeſtly represented to them the certain Deſtruction they were running into; told them they had suffer'd such Hardships upon that very Spot, that they could, without any Spirit of Prophesy, tell them, that they would be ſtarv'd, or be murder'd, and bad them consider of it.

The Men reply'd audaciously, they should be ſtarv'd if they ſtay'd here, for they could not work, and would not work; and they could but be ſtarv'd Abroad, and if they were murder'd, there was an End of them, they had no Wives or Children to cry after them; and in short, inſiſted importunately upon their Demand, declaring, that they would go, whether they would give them any Arms or no.

The *Spaniards* told them, with great Kindness, that if they were resolv'd to go, they should not go like naked Men, and be in no Condition to defend themselves; and that tho' they could ill spare their Fire-Arms, having not enough for themselves, yet they would let them have two Muskets, a Piſtol, and a Cutlash, and each Man a Hatchet, which they thought was sufficient for them.

In a Word, they accepted the Offer, and having baked them Bread enough to serve them a Month, and given them as much Goats-Flesh as they could eat while it was sweet, and a great Basket full of dry'd Grapes, a Pot full of fresh Water, and a young Kid alive to kill, they boldly set out in a Canoe for a Voyage over the Sea, where it was at leaſt 40 Miles broad.

The Boat was indeed a large one, and would have very

well carry'd fifteen or twenty Men; and, therefore, was rather too big for them to manage: But as they had a fair Breeze, and the Flood-Tide with them, they did well enough: They had made a Maſt of a long Pole, and a Sail of four large Goat-Skins dry'd, which they had sow'd or lac'd together; and away they went merrily enough; the *Spaniards* call'd after them, *Bon Veyajo*; and no Man ever thought of seeing them any more,

The *Spaniards* would often say to one another, and the two honeſt *English* Men who remain'd behind, how quietly and comfortably they liv'd now those three turbulent Fellows were gone; as for their ever coming again, that was the remoteſt Thing from their Thoughts that could be imagin'd; when behold, after two and twenty Days Absence, one of the *English* Men being abroad upon his Planting-Work, sees three ſtrange Men coming towards him at a Diſtance, with Guns upon their Shoulders.

Away runs the *English Man*, as if he was bewitch'd, comes frighted and amaz'd to the Governour *Spaniard*, and tells him they were all undone, for there were Strangers landed upon the Island, he could not tell who: The *Spaniard*, pausing a while, says to him, How do you mean, you cannot tell who? They are the Savages to be sure. No, no, says the *English* Man, they are Men in Cloaths with Arms: Nay, then, says the *Spaniard*, Why are you concern'd? If they are not Savages, they muſt be Friends, for there is no Chriſtian Nation upon Earth but will do us Good rather than Harm.

While they were debating thus, comes the three *English* Men, and ſtanding without the Wood, which was new planted, hallo'd to them; they presently knew their Voices, and so all the Wonder of that kind ceas'd. But now the Admiration was turn'd upon another Queſtion, (*viz.*) what could be the Matter, and what made them come back again?

It was not long before they brought the Men in, and enquiring where they had been, and what they had been doing, they gave them a full Account of their Voyage in a few Words, (*viz.*) That they reach'd the Land in two Days, or something less, but finding the People alarm'd at their coming, and preparing with Bows and Arrows to fight them, they durst not go on Shore, but sail'd on to the Northward six or seven Hours, till they came to a great Opening, by which they perceiv'd, that the Land they saw from our Island was not the Main, but an Island; that entring that Opening of the Sea, they saw another Island on the Right-Hand North, and several more West; and being resolv'd to land somewhere, they put over to one of the Islands which lay West, and went boldly on Shore; that they found the People very courteous and friendly to them, and that they gave them several Roots and some dry'd Fish, and appear'd very sociable; and the Women, as well as the Men, were very forward to supply them with any thing they could get for them to eat, and brought it to them a great Way upon their Heads.

They continu'd here four Days, and enquir'd, as well as they could of them by Signs, what Nations were this Way and that Way; and were told of several fierce and terrible People that liv'd almost every Way, who, as they made Signs to them, used to eat Men. But as for themselves, they said, that they never eat Men or Women, except only such as they took in the Wars, and then they own'd that they made a great Feast, and eat their Prisoners.

The *English* Men enquir'd when they had a Feast of that Kind, and they told him about two Moons ago, pointing to the Moon, and then to two Fingers; and that their great King had two hundred Prisoners now, which he had taken in his War; and they were feeding them to make them fat for the next Feast. The *English* Men seem'd mighty desirous to see those Prisoners, but the other mistaking them, thought they were desirous to have some of them to carry away for their own eating. So they beckon'd to them, pointing to the setting of the Sun, and then to the rising, which was to signify, that the next Morning at Sun-rising they would bring some for them; and accordingly the next Morning they brought down five Women and eleven Men, and gave them to the *English* Men, to carry with them on their Voyage, just as we would bring so many Cows and Oxen down to a Sea-Port Town, to victual a Ship.

As brutish and barbarous as these Fellows were at Home, their Stomachs turn'd at this Sight, and they did not know what to do; to refuse the Prisoners, would have been the highest Affront to the savage Gentry that offer'd them; and what to do with them they knew not; however, upon some Debates, they resolv'd to accept of them, and in Return they gave the Savages that brought them one of their Hatchets, an old Key, a Knife, and six or seven of their Bullets, which, tho' they did not understand, they seem'd extremely pleas'd with: And then tying the poor Creatures Hands behind them, they (the People) dragg'd the poor Prisoners into the Boat for our Men.

The *English* Men were oblig'd to come away as soon as they had them, or else they that gave them this noble Present would certainly have expected that they should have gone to work with them, have kill'd two or three of them the next Morning, and perhaps have invited the Donors to Dinner.

But having taken their Leave with all the Respects and

Thanks that could well pass between People, where on either Side they underſtood not one Word they could say, they put off with their Boat, and came back towards the firſt Island, where, when they arriv'd, they set eight of their Prisoners at Liberty, there being too many of them for their Occasion.

In their Voyage, they endeavour'd to have some Communication with their Prisoners, but it was impossible to make them underſtand any Thing; nothing they could say to them, or give them, or do for them, but was look'd upon as going about to murder them. They firſt of all unbound them, but the poor Creatures skream'd at that, especially the Women, as if they had juſt felt the Knife at their Throats; for they immediately concluded they were unbound on purpose to be kill'd.

If they gave them any Thing to eat, it was the same Thing; then they concluded it was for fear they should sink in Flesh, and so not be fat enough to kill. If they look'd at one of them more particularly, the Party presently concluded, it was to see whether he or she was fatteſt and fitteſt to kill. Nay, after they had brought them quite over, and began to use them kindly, and treat them well, ſtill they expected every Day to make a Dinner or a Supper for their new Maſters.

When the three Wanderers had given this unaccountable Hiſtory, or Journal of their Voyage, the *Spaniard* ask'd them, Where their new Family was? and being told that they had brought them on Shore, and put them into one of their Huts, and were come up to beg some Victuals for them; they (the *Spaniards*) and the other two *English* Men, that is to say, the whole Colony, resolv'd to go all down to the Place and see them, and did so, and *Friday's* Father with them.

When they came into the Hut, *there they sate* all bound; for when they had brought them on Shore, they bound their Hands that they might not take the Boat and make their Escape. There, I say, they sate, all of them ſtark naked: *Firſt*, There were three Men, luſty comely Fellows, well shap'd, ſtrait and fair Limbs, about thirty to thirty five Years of Age; and five Women, whereof two might be from thirty to forty, two more not above four or five and twenty, and the fifth, a tall comely Maiden about sixteen or seventeen: The Women were well favour'd agreeable Persons, both in Shape and Features, only tawny, and two of them, had they been perfect White, would have pass'd for very handsome Women even in *London* itself, having pleasant agreeable Countenances, and of a very modeſt Behaviour, especially when they came afterwards to be cloath'd, and dress'd, as they call'd it, tho' the Dress was very indifferent it muſt be confess'd; of which hereafter.

The Sight, you may be sure, was something uncouth to our *Spaniards*, who were (to give them a juſt Character) Men of the beſt Behaviour, of the moſt calm, sedate Tempers, and perfect Good-humour that ever I met with, and in particular, of the moſt Modeſty, as will presently appear: I say, the Sight was very uncouth, to see two naked Men and five naked Women, all together bound, and in the moſt miserable Circumſtances that Human Nature could be suppos'd to be, (*viz.*) to be expecting every Moment to be dragg'd out, and have their Brains knock'd out, and then to be eaten up like a Calf that is kill'd for a Dainty.

The firſt Thing they did, was to cause the old *Indian*, *Friday's* Father, to go in and see firſt if he knew any of them, and then if he underſtood any of their Speech: As soon as the old Man came in, he look'd seriously at them, but knew none of them; neither could any of them understand a Word he said, or a Sign he could make, except one of the Women.

However, this was enough to answer the End, which was to satisfy them, that the Men into whose Hands they were fallen, were Christians; that they abhorr'd eating of Men or Women, and that they might be sure they would not be kill'd: As soon as they were assur'd of this, they discover'd such Joy, and by such aukward, and several Ways, as is hard to describe; for it seems they were of several Nations.

The Woman, who was their Interpreter, was bid in the next Place to ask them, if they were willing to be Servants, and to work for the Men who had brought them away, to save their Lives; at which they all fell a Dancing; and presently one fell to taking up this, and another that, any Thing that lay next, to carry on their Shoulders, to intimate that they were willing to work.

The Governor, who found, that the having Women among them would presently be attended with some Inconvenience, and might occasion some Strife, and perhaps Blood; ask'd the three Men, what they intended to do with these Women, and how they intended to use them; whether as Servants, or as Women? One of the *Englishmen* answer'd very boldly and readily, That they would use them as both. To which the Governor said, I am not going to restrain you from it, you are your own Masters as to that: But this I think is but just, for avoiding Disorders and Quarrels among you; and I desire it of you, for that Reason only, *viz.* That you will all engage, that if any of you take any of these Women, as a Woman or Wife, that he shall take but one; and that having taken one, none else should touch her; for tho' we cannot marry any of you, yet 'tis but reasonable, that while you stay here, the Woman any of you takes, should be maintain'd by the Man that takes her, and should be his Wife; I mean, says he, while he continues here, and that none else shall have any Thing to do with her: All this appear'd so just, that every one agreed to it without any Difficulty.

Then the *Englishmen* ask'd the *Spaniards*, if they design'd to take any of them? But every one of them answer'd, NO: Some of them said, they had Wives in *Spain*, and the others did not like Women that were not Christians; and all together declar'd, that they would not touch one of them; which was an Instance of such Virtue, as I have not met with in all my Travels. On the other Hand, to be short, the five *Englishmen* took them every one a Wife, that is to say, a temporary Wife; and so they set up a new Form of Living; for the *Spaniards* and *Friday's* Father liv'd in my old Habitation, which they had enlarg'd exceedingly within. The three Servants which were taken in the late Battle of the Savages, liv'd with them; and these carry'd on the main Part of the Colony, supplying all the rest with Food, and assisting them in any Thing as they could, or as they found Necessity requir'd.

But the Wonder of this Story was, how five such refractory ill match'd Fellows should agree about these Women, and that two of them should not pitch upon the same Woman, especially seeing two or three of them were without Comparison, more agreeable than the other: But they took a good Way enough to prevent quarrelling among themselves; for they set the five Women by themselves in one of their Huts, and they went all into the other Hut, and drew Lots among them, who should chuse first.

He that drew to chuse first, went away by himself to the Hut where the poor naked Creatures were, and fetch'd out her he chose; and it was worth observing, that he that chose first took her that was reckon'd the homeliest, and the oldest of the five, which made Mirth enough among the rest; and even the *Spaniards* laugh'd at it: But the Fellow consider'd better than any of them, that it was Application and Business that they were to expect Assistance in, as much as any Thing else; and she prov'd the best Wife of all the Parcel.

When the poor Women saw themselves set in a Row thus, and fetch'd out one by one, the Terrors of their Condition return'd upon them again, and they firmly believ'd that they were now a going to be devour'd; accordingly, when the *English* Sailor came in and fetch'd out one of them; the rest set up a most lamentable Cry, and hung about her, and took their Leave of her with such Agonies and such Affection, as would have griev'd the hardest Heart in the World; nor was it possible for the *Englishmen* to satisfy them, that they were not to be immediately murder'd, 'till they fetch'd the old Man, *Friday*'s Father, who immediately let them know that the five Men, who had fetch'd them out one by one, had chosen them for their Wives.

When they had done, and the Fright the Women were in was a little over, the Men went to Work, and the *Spaniards* came and help'd them; and in a few Hours they had built them every one a new Hut or Tent for their Lodging apart; for those they had already, were crowded with their Tools, Houshold-Stuff, and Provision. The three wicked Ones had pitch'd farthest off, and the two honest Ones nearer, but both on the North Shore of the Island, so that they continu'd separate as before: And thus my

Island was peopled in three Places; and, as I might say, three Towns were begun to be planted.

And here 'tis very well worth observing, That as it often happens in the World (what the wise Ends of God's Providence are in such a Disposition of Things, I cannot say) the two honest Fellows had the two worst Wives, and the three Reprobates, that were scarce worth hanging, that were fit for nothing, and neither seem'd born to do themselves Good, or any one else, had three clever, diligent, careful, and ingenious Wives; not that the two first were ill Wives, as to their Temper or Humour; for all the five were most willing, quiet, passive, and subjected Creatures, rather like Slaves than Wives; but my Meaning is, they were not alike capable, ingenious, or industrious, or alike cleanly and neat.

Another Observation I must make, to the Honour of a diligent Application on one Hand, and to the Disgrace of a slothful, negligent, idle Temper, on the other, that when I came to the Place, and view'd the several Improvements Plantings, and Management of the several little Colonies, the two Men had so far out-gone the three, that there was no Comparison. They had indeed both of them as much Ground laid out for Corn as they wanted; and the Reason was, because, according to my Rule, Nature dictated, that it was to no Purpose to sow more Corn than they wanted, but the Difference of the Cultivation, of the Planting, of the Fences, and indeed of every Thing else was easy to be seen at first View.

The two Men had innumerable young Trees planted about their Huts, that when you came to the Place, nothing was to be seen but a Wood, and tho' they had twice had their Plantation demolish'd, once by their own Countrymen, and once by the Enemy, as shall be shewn in its

Place; yet they had reſtor'd all again, and every Thing was thriving and flourishing about them; they had Grapes planted in Order, and manag'd like a Vineyard, tho' they had themselves never seen any Thing of that Kind; and by their good ordering their Vines, their Grapes were as good again as any of the others. They had also found themselves out a Retreat in the thickeſt Part of the Woods, where, though there was not a natural Cave, as I had found, yet they made one with incessant Labour of their Hands, and where when the Mischief which follow'd happen'd, they secur'd their Wives and Children, so as they could never be found; they having by ſticking innumerable Stakes and Poles of the Wood, which, as I said, grew so easily, made the Wood unpassable, except in some Places, where they climb'd up to get over the outside Part, and then went on by Ways of their own leaving.

As to the three Reprobates, as I juſtly call them, tho' they were much civiliz'd by their new Settlement, compar'd to what they were before, and were not so quarrelsom, having not the same Opportunity; yet one of the certain Companions of a profligate Mind never left them, and that was their Idleness. It is true, they planted Corn, and made Fences; but *Solomon*'s Words were never better verified than in them. *I went by the Vineyard of the Slothful, and it was all over-grown with Thorns*; for when the *Spaniards* came to view their Crop, they could not see it in some Places for Weeds; The Hedge had several Gaps in it, where the wild Goats had gotten in, and eaten up the Corn; perhaps, here and there, a dead Bush was cramm'd in, to ſtop them out for the Present, but it was only shutting the Stable Door after the Steed was ſtoln. Whereas, when they look'd on the Colony of the other two, there was the very Face of Induſtry and Success upon all they did; there was not a Weed to be seen in all their Corn, or a Gap in any of their Hedges: And they on the other Hand verified *Solomon*'s Words in another Place, *That the diligent Hand makes rich*; for every Thing grew and thriv'd, and they had Plenty within and without; they had more tame Cattle than the other, more Utensils and Necessaries within Doors, and yet more Pleasure and Diversion too.

It is true, the Wives of the three were very handy and cleanly within Doors, and having learn'd the *English* Ways of Dressing and Cooking from one of the other *English* Men, who, as I said, was Cook's-mate on board the Ship, they dress'd their Husbands Victuals very nicely and well; whereas the other could not be brought to understand it; but then the Husband, who, as I say, had been Cook's-mate, did it himself; but as for the Husbands of the three Wives, they loyter'd about, fetch'd Turtles Eggs, and caught Fish, and Birds, in a Word, any thing but Labour, and they far'd accordingly. The Diligent liv'd well and comfortably, and the Slothful liv'd hard and beggarly; and so I believe, generally speaking, it is all over the World.

But now I come to a Scene, different from all that had happen'd before, either to them, or to me; and the Original of the Story was this.

Early one Morning there came on Shore five or six Canoes of *Indians*, or *Savages*, call them which you please; and there is no room to doubt that they came upon the old Errand of feeding upon their Slaves: But that Part was now so familiar to the *Spaniards*, and to our Men too, that they did not concern themselves about it, as I did; but having been made sensible by their Experience, that their only Business was to lye concealed, and that if they were not seen by any of the Savages, they would go off again quietly when their Business was done, having as yet not the least Notion of there being any Inhabitants in the Island; I say, having been made sensible of this, they had nothing to do but to give Notice to all the three Plantations, to keep within Doors, and not shew themselves, only placing a Scout in a proper Place, to give Notice when the Boats went to Sea again.

This was without doubt very right; but a Disaster spoil'd all these Measures, and made it known among the Savages, that there were Inhabitants there, which was in the End the Desolation of almost the whole Colony; after the Canoes with the Savages were gone off, the *Spaniards* peep'd abroad again, and some of them had the Curiosity to go to the Place where they had been, to see what they had been doing: Here, to their great Surprize, they found three Savages left behind, and lying fast asleep upon the Ground; it was suppos'd, they had either been so gorg'd with their inhuman Feast, that, like Beasts, they were asleep, and would not stir when the others went, or they were wander'd into the Woods, and did not come back in time to be taken in.

The *Spaniards* were greatly surpriz'd at this Sight, and perfectly at a Loss what to do; the *Spaniard* Governour, as it happen'd, was with them, and his Advice was ask'd, but he profess'd he knew not what to do; as for Slaves, they had enough already, and as to killing them, they were none of them inclin'd to that; the *Spaniard* Governour told me, they could not think of shedding innocent Blood, for as to them, the poor Creatures had done them no Wrong, invaded none of their Property, and they thought they had no just Quarrel against them, to take away their Lives.

And here I must, in Justice to these *Spaniards*, observe, that let the Accounts of *Spanish* Cruelty in *Mexico* and *Peru*, be what they will, I never met with seventeen Men of any Nation whatsoever, in any foreign Country, who were so universally Modest, Temperate, Virtuous, so very Good-humour'd, and so Courteous as these *Spaniards*; and as to Cruelty, they had nothing of it in their very Nature, no Inhumanity, no Barbarity, no outragious Passions, and yet all of them Men of great Courage and Spirit.

Their Temper and Calmness had appear'd in their bearing the unsufferable Usage of the three *English* Men; and their Justice and Humanity appear'd now in the Case of the Savages, as above. After some Consultation, they resolv'd upon this, that they would lie still a while longer, 'till, if possible, these three Men might be gone; but then the Governour *Spaniard* recollected, that the three Savages had no Boat, and that if they were left to rove about the Island, they would certainly discover that there were Inhabitants in it, and so they should be undone that Way.

Upon this, they went back again, and there lay the Fellows fast asleep still, so they resolv'd to waken them, and take them Prisoners, and they did so; the poor Fellows were strangely frighted when they were seiz'd upon and bound, and afraid, like the Women, that they should be murder'd and eaten; for it seems those People think all the World does as they do, eating Mens Flesh; but they were soon made easy as to that, and away they carry'd them.

It was very happy to them that they did not carry them Home to their Castle, I mean to my Palace under the Hill; but they carry'd them first to the Bower, where was the chief of their Country-work, such as the keeping the Goats, the planting the Corn, *&c.* and afterwards, they carry'd them to the Habitation of the two *English* Men.

Here they were set to work, tho' it was not much they had for them to do; and whether it was by Negligence in guarding them, or that they thought the Fellows could not mend themselves, I know not, but one of them run away, and taking into the Woods, they could never hear of him more.

They had good Reason to believe he got Home again soon after, in some other Boats or Canoes of Savages, who came on Shore three or four Weeks afterwards, and who, carrying on their Revels as usual, went off again in two Days time: This Thought terrify'd them exceedingly; for they concluded, and that not without good Cause indeed, that if this Fellow came safe Home among his Comrades, he would certainly give them an Account, that there were People in the Island, as also how few and weak they were; for this Savage, as I observ'd before, had never been told, and it was very happy he had not, how many they were, or where they liv'd; nor had he ever seen or heard the Fire of any of their Guns, much less had they shewn him any of their other retir'd Places; such as the Cave in the Valley, or the new Retreat which the two *English* Men had made, *and the like.*

The first Testimony they had that this Fellow had given Intelligence of them, was, that about two Months after this, six Canoes of Savages, with about seven, or eight, or ten Men in a Canoe, came rowing along the North Side of the Island, where they never used to come before, and landed about an Hour after Sunrise, at a convenient Place, about a Mile from the Habitation of the two *Englishmen*, where this escap'd Man had been kept: As the *Spaniard* Governor said, had they been all there, the Damage would not have been so much, for not a Man of them would have escap'd; but the Case differ'd now very much, for two Men to fifty was too much odds: The two Men had the happiness to discover them about a League off, so that it was above an Hour before they landed, and as they landed a Mile from their Huts, it was some time before they could come at them: Now having great Reason to believe that they were betray'd, the first Thing they did, was to bind the two Slaves which were left, and cause two of the three Men, who they brought with the Women, who it seems prov'd very faithful to them, to lead them with their two Wives, and whatever they could carry away with them, to their retir'd Place in the Woods, which I have spoken of above, and there to bind the two Fellows Hand and Foot 'till they heard farther.

In the next Place, seeing the Savages were all come on Shore, and that they bent their Course directly that Way, they open'd the Fences where their Milch-Goats were kept, and drove them all out, leaving their Goats to straggle into the Woods whither they pleas'd, that the Savages might think they were all bred wild; but the Rogue who came with them was too cunning for that, and gave them an Account of it all; for they went directly to the Place.

When the two poor frighted Men had secur'd their Wives and Goods, they sent the other Slave they had of the three, who came with the Women, and who was at their Place by Accident, away to the *Spaniards*, with all Speed, to give them the Alarm, and desire speedy Help; and in the mean Time they took their Arms, and what Ammunition they had, and retreated towards the Place in the Wood, where their Wives were sent, keeping at a Distance, yet so that they might see, if possible, which Way the Savages took.

They had not gone far, but that, from a rising Ground, they could see the little Army of their Enemies come on directly to their Habitation, and in a Moment more, could see all their Huts and Houshold-Stuff flaming up together, to their great Grief and Mortification; for they had a very great Loss, to them irretrievable, at least for some Time. They kept their Station for a while, 'till they found the Savages, like wild Beasts, spread themselves all over the Place, rummaging every Way, and every Place they could think of, in Search for Prey, and in particular for the People, of whom it now plainly appear'd they had Intelligence.

The two *Englishmen* seeing this, thinking themselves not secure where they stood, because as it was likely some of the wild People might come that Way, so they might come too many together, thought it proper to make another Retreat about half a Mile farther, believing, as it afterwards happen'd, that the farther they stroll'd, the fewer would be together.

The next Halt was at the Entrance into a very thick grown Part of the Woods, and where an old Trunk of a Tree stood, which was hollow and vastly large; and in this Tree they both took their Standing, resolving to see there what might offer.

They had not stood there long, but two of the Savages appear'd running directly that Way, as if they had already had Notice where they stood, and were coming up to attack them; and a little Way farther, they spy'd three more coming after them, and five more beyond them, all coming the same Way; besides which, they saw seven or eight more at a Distance, running another Way; for in a Word, they ran every Way like Sportsmen beating for their Game.

The poor Men were now in great Perplexity, whether they should ſtand and keep their Poſture, or fly: But after a very short Debate with themselves, they consider'd, that if the Savages rang'd the Country thus before Help came, they might perhaps find out their Retreat in the Woods, then all would be loſt; so they resolv'd to ſtand them there: And if they were too many to deal with, then they would get up to the Top of the Tree, from whence they doubted not to defend themselves, *Fire excepted*, as long as their Ammunition laſted, tho' all the Savages that were landed, which was near fifty, were to attack them.

Having resolv'd upon this, they next consider'd whether they should fire at the firſt two, or wait for the three, and so take the middle Party, by which the two and the five that follow'd would be separated; and they resolv'd to let the two firſt pass by, unless they should spy them in the Tree, and come to attack them. The two firſt Savages also confirm'd them in this Regulation, by turning a little from them towards another Part of the Wood; but the three, and the five after them, came forwards directly to the Tree, as if they had known the *Englishmen* were there.

Seeing them come soſtrait towards them, they resolv'd to take them in a Line, as they came; and as they resolv'd to fire but one at a time, perhaps the firſt Shot might hit them all three, to which Purpose, the Man who was to fire, put three or four small Bullets into his Piece, and having a fair Loop-hole, as it were, from a broken Hole in the Tree, he took a sure Aim, without being seen, waiting till they were within about thirty Yards of the Tree, so that he could not miss.

While they were thus waiting, and the Savages came on, they plainly saw, that one of the three was the Run-away Savage that had escap'd from them, and they both knew him distinctly, and resolv'd that, if possible, he should not escape, tho' they should both fire; so the other stood ready with his Peice, that if he did not drop at the first Shot, he should be sure to have a second.

But the first was too good a Marksman to miss his Aim; for as the Savages kept near one another, a little behind in a Line, in a Word, he fir'd, and hit two of them directly: The foremost was kill'd outright, being shot in the Head: The second, which was the Run-away *Indian*, was shot thro' the Body, and fell, but was not quite dead: And the third had a little Scratch in the Shoulder, perhaps by the same Ball that went thro' the Body of the second, and being dreadfully frighted, tho' not much hurt, sate down upon the Ground, skreaming and yelling in a hideous manner.

The five that were behind, more frighted with the Noise than sensible of the Danger, stood still at first; for the Woods made the sound a thousand Times bigger than it really was; the Echo's rattling from one Side to another, and the Fowls rising from all Parts, skreaming, and making, every Sort, a several Kind of Noise, according to their Kind, just as it was when I fir'd the first Gun that perhaps was ever shot off in that Place since it was an Island.

However, all being silent again, and they not knowing what the Matter was, came on unconcern'd, 'till they came to the Place where their Companions lay in a Condition miserable enough: And here the poor ignorant Creatures, not sensible that they were within Reach of the same Mischief, stood all of a Huddle over the wounded Man, talking, and, as may be suppos'd, enquiring of him, how he came to be hurt; and who, 'tis very rational to believe, told them, that a Flash of Fire first, and immediately after that, Thunder from their Gods, had kill'd those two and wounded him: This, I say, is rational; for nothing is more certain than that, as they saw no Man near them, so they had never heard a Gun in all their Lives, or so much as heard of a Gun; neither knew they any Thing of killing or wounding, at a Distance, with Fire and Bullets; if they had, one might reasonably believe, they would not have stood so unconcern'd, in viewing the Fate of their Fellows, without some Apprehension of their own.

Our two Men, tho' as they confess'd to me, it griev'd them to be oblig'd to kill so many poor Creatures, who at the same Time had no Notion of their Danger; yet having them all thus in their Power, and the first having loaded his Piece again, resolv'd to let fly both together among them; and singling out, by Agreement, which to aim at, they shot together, and kill'd or very much wounded four of them; the fifth frighted even to Death, tho' not hurt, fell with the rest: so that our Men seeing them all fall together, thought they had kill'd them all.

The Belief that the Savages were all kill'd, made our two Men come boldly out from the Tree before they had charg'd their Guns again, which was a wrong Step; and they were under some Surprize when they came to the Place, and found no less than four of the Men alive, and of them two very little hurt, and one not at all: This oblig'd them to fall upon them with the Stocks of their Muskets; and first they made sure of the Run-away Savage, that had been the Cause of all the Mischief, and of another that was hurt in his Knee, and put them out of their Pain; then the Man that was not hurt at all, came and kneel'd down to them, with his two Hands held up, and made piteous Moans to them by Gestures and Signs, for his Life; but could not say one Word to them that they could underſtand.

However, they sign'd to him to sit down at the Foot of a Tree thereby; and one of the *English* Men, with a Piece of Rope-Twine which he had, by great Chance, in his Pocket, ty'd his two Feet faſt together, and his two Hands behind him, and there they left him; and, with what Speed they could, made after the other two, which were gone before; fearing they, or any more of them, should find the Way to their cover'd Place in the Woods, where their Wives, and the few Goods they had left, lay. They came once in Sight of the two Men, but it was at a great Distance; however, they had the Satisfaction to see them cross over a Valley towards the Sea, the quite contrary Way from that which led to their Retreat, which they were afraid of; and being satisfy'd with that, they went back to the Tree, where they left their Prisoner, who, as they suppos'd, was deliver'd by his Comrades; for he was gone, and the two Pieces of Rope-Yarn, with which they had bound him, lay juſt at the Foot of the Tree.

They were now in as a great a Concern as before, not knowing what Course to take, or how near the Enemy might be, or in what Numbers; so they resolv'd to go away to the Place where their Wives were, to see if all was well there, and to make them easy, who were in Fright enough to be sure; for tho' the Savages were their own Country Folk, yet they were moſt terribly afraid of them, and perhaps the more, for the Knowledge they had of them.

When they came there, they found the Savages had been in the Wood, and very near that Place, but had not found it; for it was indeed inaccessible, by the Trees ſtanding so thick, *as before*, had not the Persons seeking it been directed by those that knew it, which these did not; they found therefore every Thing very safe, only the Women in a terrible Fright: While they were here, they had the Comfort to have seven of the *Spaniards* come to their Assistance; the other ten, with their Servants, and old *Friday*, I mean *Friday*'s Father, were gone in a Body to defend their Bower, and the Corn, and Cattle that was kept there, in Case the Savages should have rov'd over to that Side of the Country; but they did not spread so far. With the seven *Spaniards* came one of the three Savages, who, as I said, were their Prisoners formerly; and with them also came the Savage, who the *English* Men had left bound Hand and Foot at the Tree; for it seems they came that Way, saw the Slaughter of the seven Men, and unbound the eighth, and brought him along with them; where, however, they were oblig'd to bind him again, as they had the two others, who were left when the third run away.

The Prisoners began now to be a Burden to them; and they were so afraid of their escaping, that they were once resolving to kill them all, believing they were under an absolute Necessity to do so, for their own Preservation: However, the *Spaniard* Governour would not consent to it, but order'd for the present, that they should be sent out of the Way to my old Cave in the Valley, and be kept there with two *Spaniards* to guard them, and give them Food for their Subsistence, which was done; and they were bound there Hand and Foot for that Night.

When the *Spaniards* came, the two *English* Men were so encourag'd, that thy could not satisfy themselves to stay any longer there; but taking five of the *Spaniards*, and themselves, with four Muskets and a Pistol among them, and two stout Quarter-Staves, away they went in

Quest of the Savages. And first they came to the Tree where the Men lay that had been kill'd; but it was easy to see, that some more of the Savages had been there; for they had attempted to carry their dead Men away, and had dragg'd two of them a good Way, but had given it over. From thence they advanc'd to the first rising Ground, where they stood, and saw their Camp destroy'd, and where they had the Mortification still to see some of the Smoak; but neither could they here see any of the Savages: They then resolv'd, tho' with all possible Caution, to go forward towards their ruin'd Plantation. But a little before they came thither, coming in Sight of the Sea Shore, they saw plainly the Savages all embarking again in their Canoes, in order to be gone.

They seem'd sorry at first; and there was no Way to come at them, to give them a parting Blow: But upon the whole, were very well satisfy'd to be rid of them.

The poor *English* Men being now twice ruin'd, and all their Improvement destroy'd, the rest all agreed to come and help them rebuild, and to assist them with needful Supplies. Their three Countrymen, who were not yet noted for having the least Inclination to do any Good, yet as soon as they heard of it (for they living remote Eastward, knew nothing of the Matter 'till all was over) came and offer'd their Help and Assistance, and did very friendly work for several Days, to restore their Habitation, and make Necessaries for them: And thus, in a little Time, they were set upon their Legs again.

About two Days after this, they had the farther Satisfaction of seeing three of the Savages Canoes come driving on Shore, and at some Distance from them, two drown'd Men; by which they had Reason to believe, that they had met with a Storm at Sea, and had overset some of them; for it had blown very hard the very Night after they went off.

However, as some might miscarry, so on the other Hand, enough of them escap'd to inform the rest, as well of what they had done, as of what had happen'd to them; and to whet them on to another Enterprize of the same Nature, which they, it seems, resolv'd to attempt, with sufficient Force to carry all before them; for except what the first Man had told them of Inhabitants, they could say little to it of their own Knowledge; for they never saw one Man, and the Fellow being kill'd that had affirm'd it, they had no other Witness to confirm it to them.

It was five or six Months after this, before they heard any more of the Savages; in which Time our Men were in Hopes they had either forgot their former bad Luck, or given over the Hopes of better; when on a sudden they were invaded with a most formidable Fleet, of no less than eight and twenty Canoes full of Savages, arm'd with Bows and Arrows, great Clubs, wooden Swords, and such like Engines of War; and they brought such Numbers with them, that in short, it put all our People into the utmost Consternation.

As they came on Shore in the Evening, and at the Easter-most Side of the Island, our Men had that Night to consult and consider what to do; and, in the first Place, knowing that their being entirely conceal'd, was their only Safety before, and would much more be so now, while the Number of their Enemies was so great, they therefore resolv'd first of all to take down the Huts which were built for the two *English* Men, and drive away their Goats to the old Cave; because they suppos'd the Savages would go directly thither, as soon as it was Day, to play the old Game over again, tho' they did not now land within two Leagues of it.

In the next Place, they drove away all the Flock of Goats they had at the old Bower, as I call'd it, which belong'd to the *Spaniards*; and in short, left as little Appearance of Inhabitants any where as was possible; and the next Morning early they posted themselves with all their Force at the Plantation of the two Men, waiting for their Coming: As they guess'd, so it happen'd; these new Invaders leaving their Canoes at the East End of the Island, came ranging along the Shore directly towards the Place, to the Number of two hundred and fifty, as near as our Men could judge. Our Army was but small indeed; but that which was worse, they had not Arms for all their Number neither: The whole Account it seems, stood thus: First, as to Men.

17 *Spaniards*.
5 *English* Men.
1 Old *Friday*, or *Friday*'s Father.
3, the three Slaves taken with the Women, who prov'd very faithful.
3 Other Slaves who liv'd with the *Spaniards*.

To arm these, they had,

11 Muskets.
5 Pistols.
3 Fowling-Pieces.
5 Muskets or Fowling-Pieces, which were taken by me from the mutinous Seamen, who I reduc'd.
2 Swords, 3 old Halberds.

To their Slaves they did not give either Musket or Fuzee, but they had every one a Halberd, or a long Staff, like a Quarter-Staff, with a great Spike of Iron faſten'd into each End of it, and by his Side a Hatchet; also every one of our Men had Hatchets: Two of the Women could not be prevail'd upon but they would come into the Fight, and they had Bows and Arrows, which the *Spaniards* had taken from the Savages, when the firſt Action happen'd, which I have spoken of, where the *Indians* fought with one another, and the Women Hatchets too.

The *Spaniard* Governour, who I have describ'd so often, commanded the whole; and *William Atkins*, who, tho' a dreadful Fellow for Wickedness, was a moſt daring bold Fellow, commanded under him. The Savages came forward like Lyons, and our Men, which was the worſt of their Fate, had no Advantage in their Situation; only that *Will. Atkins*, who now prov'd a moſt useful Fellow, with six Men, was planted juſt behind a small Thicket of Bushes, as an advanc'd Guard, with Orders to let the firſt of them pass by, and then fire into the Middle of them; and as soon as he had fir'd, to make his Retreat as nimbly as he could round a Part of the Wood, and so come in behind the *Spaniards* where they ſtood, having a Thicket of Trees also before them.

When the Savages came on, they run ſtraggling about every Way in Heaps, out of all manner of Order, and *W. Atkins* let about fifty of them pass by him, then seeing the reſt come in a very thick Throng, he orders three of his Men to fire, having loaded their Muskets with six or seven Bullets a piece, about as big as large Pistol Bullets. How many they kill'd or wounded they knew not, but the Conſternation and Surprize was inexpressible among the Savages; they were frighted to the laſt Degree, to hear such a dreadful Noise, and see their Men kill'd, and others hurt, but see no Body that did it; when in the Middle of their Fright, *W. Atkins*, and his other three, let fly again among the thickest of them; and in less than a Minute the first three, being loaded again, gave them a third Volley.

Had *W. Atkins* and his Men retir'd immediately, as soon as they had fir'd, as they were order'd to do; or had the rest of the Body been at Hand to have pour'd in their Shot continually, the Savages had been effectually routed; for the Terror that was among them, came principally from this, (*viz.*) That they were kill'd by the Gods with Thunder and Lightning, and could see no Body that hurt them; but *W. Atkins* staying to load again, discover'd the Cheat. Some of the Savages who were at a Distance, spying them, came upon them behind, and tho' *Atkins* and his Men fir'd at them also, two or three Times, and kill'd above twenty, retiring as fast as they could, yet they wounded *Atkins* himself, and kill'd one of his Fellow *Englishmen* with their Arrows, as they did afterwards one *Spaniard*, and one of the *Indian* Slaves who came with the Women; this Slave was a most gallant Fellow, and fought most desperately, killing five of them with his own Hand, having no Weapon, but one of the arm'd Staves and a Hatchet.

Our Men being thus hard laid at, *Atkins* wounded, and two other Men kill'd, retreated to a rising Ground in the Wood; and the *Spaniards*, after firing three Vollies upon them, retreated also; for their Number was so great, and they were so desperate, that tho' above fifty of them were kill'd, and more than so many wounded, yet they came on in the Teeth of our Men, fearless of Danger, and shot their Arrows like a Cloud; and it was observ'd, that their wounded Men, who were not quite disabled, were made outrageous by their Wounds, and fought like Mad-men.

When our Men retreated, they left the *Spaniard* and the *Englishman* that was kill'd behind them; and the Savages, when they came up to them, kill'd them over again in a wretched Manner, breaking the Arms, Legs, and Heads, with their Clubs and wooden Swords, like true Savages: But finding our Men were gone, they did not seem to pursue them, but drew themselves up in a kind of a Ring, which is, it seems, their Custom, and shouted twice in Token of their Victory: After which, they had the Mortification to see several of their wounded Men fall, dying with the meer Loss of Blood.

The *Spaniard* Governor having drawn his little Body up together upon a rising Ground, *Atkins*, tho' he was wounded, would ha' had him march'd and charg'd them again altogether at once: But the *Spaniards* reply'd, Seignior *Atkins*, you see how their wounded Men fight, let them alone till Morning; all these wounded Men will be stiff and sore with their Wounds, and faint with the Loss of Blood; and so we shall have the fewer to engage.

The Advice was good: But *Will. Atkins* reply'd merrily, That's true, Seignior, and so shall I too; and that's the Reason I would go on while I am warm. Well, Seignior *Atkins*, says the *Spaniards*, you have behav'd gallantly, and done your Part; we will fight for you, if you cannot come on, but I think it best to stay 'till Morning; so they waited.

But as it was a clear Moon-light Night, and they found the Savages in great Disorder about their dead and wounded Men, and a great Hurry and Noise among them where they lay, they afterwards resolv'd to fall upon them in the Night, especially if they could come to give them but one Volley before they were discover'd, which they had a fair Opportunity to do; for one of the two *Englishmen*, in whose Quarter it was where the Fight began, led them round between the Woods, and Sea-side Weſtward, and then turning short South, they came so near where the thickeſt of them lay, that before they were seen or heard, eight of them fir'd in among them, and did dreadful Execution upon them; in half a Minute more, eight others fir'd after them, pouring in their small Shot in such a Quantity, that abundance were kill'd and wounded; and all this while they were not able to see who hurt them, or which Way to fly.

The *Spaniards* charg'd again with the utmoſt Expedition, and then divided themselves into three Bodies, and resolv'd to fall in among them altogether: They had in each Body eight Persons, that is to say, 24, whereof were 22 Men, and the 2 Women, who by the Way fought desperately.

They divided the Fire-Arms equally in each Party, and so of the Halberds and Staves: They would have had the Women keep back, but they said they were resolv'd to die with their Husbands: Having thus form'd their little Army, they march'd out from among the Trees, and came up to the Teeth of the Enemy, shouting and hollowing as loud as they could; the Savages ſtood all together, but were in the utmoſt Confusion, hearing the Noise of our Men shouting from three Quarters together; they would have fought if they had seen us: And as soon as we came near enough to be seen, some Arrows were shot, and poor old *Friday* was wounded, tho' not dangerously: But our Men gave them no Time; but running up to them, fir'd among them three Ways, and then fell in with the But-ends of their Muskets, their Swords, arm'd Staves, and Hatchets, and laid about them so well, that, in a Word, they set up a dismal Skreaming and Howling, flying to save their Lives, which Way soever they could.

Our Men were tir'd with the Execution; and kill'd, or mortally wounded, in the two Fights, about 180 of them; the reſt, being frighted out of their Wits, scour'd through the Woods, and over the Hills, with all the Speed and Fear that nimble Feet could help them to do; and as we did not trouble ourselves much to pursue them, they got all together to the Sea Side, where they landed, and where their Canoes lay. But their Disaſter was not at an End yet; for it blew a terrible Storm of Wind that Evening from the Seaward, so that it was impossible for them to go off; nay, the Storm continuing all Night, when the Tide came up, their Canoes were moſt of them driven by the Surge of the Sea so high upon the Shore, that it requir'd infinite Toil to get them off; and some of them were even dash'd to Pieces againſt the Beach, or againſt one another.

Our Men, tho' glad of their Victory, yet got little Reſt that Night; but having refresh'd themselves as well as they could, they resolv'd to march to that Part of the Island where the Savages were fled, and see what Poſture they were in. This necessarily led them over the Place where the Fight had been, and where they found several of the poor Creatures not quite dead, and yet paſt recovering Life; a Sight disagreeable enough to generous Minds; for a truly great Man, tho' obliged by the Law of Battle to deſtroy his Enemy, takes no Delight in his Misery.

However, there was no Need to give any Orders in

this Case; for their own Savages, who were their Servants dispatch'd those poor Creatures with their Hatchets.

At length they came in View of the Place where the more miserable Remains of the Savages Army lay, where there appear'd about an hundred ſtill; their Poſture was generally sitting upon the Ground, with their Knees up towards their Mouth, and the Head put between the two Hands, leaning down upon the Knees.

When our Men came within two Musket Shot of them, the *Spaniard* Governor order'd two Muskets to be fir'd without Ball, to alarm them; this he did, that by their Countenance he might know what to expect, *viz.* Whether they were ſtill in Heart to fight, or were so heartily beaten, as to be dispirited and discourag'd, and so he might manage accordingly.

This Stratagem took; for, as soon as the Savages heard the firſt Gun, and saw the Flash of the Second, they ſtarted up upon their Feet in the greateſt Conſternation imaginable; and as our Men advanc'd swiftly towards them, they all ran skreaming and yawling away, with a kind of a howling Noise, which our Men did not underſtand, and had never heard before; and thus they ran up the Hills into the Country.

At firſt, our Men had much rather the Weather had been calm, and they had all gone away to Sea: But they did not then consider that this might probably have been the Occasion of their coming again in such Multitudes, as not to be resiſted, or, at leaſt, to come so many, and so often, as would quite desolate the Island, and ſtarve them: *Will. Atkins* therefore, who, notwithſtanding his Wound, kept always with them, prov'd the beſt Counsellor in this Case: His Advice was, to take the Advantage that offer'd, and clap in between them and their Boats, and so deprive them of the Capacity of ever returning any more to plague the Island.

They consulted long about this, and some were against it, for fear of making the Wretches fly to the Woods, and live there desperate; and so they should have them to hunt like wild Beasts, be afraid to stir out about their Business, and have their Plantations continually rifled, all their tame Goats destroy'd, and, in short, be reduc'd to a Life of continual Distress.

Will. Atkins told them, they had better have to do with a hundred Men, than with a hundred Nations: That as they must destroy their Boats, so they must destroy the Men, or be all of them destroy'd themselves. In a Word, he shew'd them the Necessity of it so plainly, that they all came into it; so they went to work immediately with the Boats, and getting some dry Wood together from a dead Tree, they try'd to set some on them on Fire, but they were so wet, that they would not burn; however, the Fire so burn'd the upper Part, that it soon made them unfit for swimming in the Sea as Boats. When the *Indians* saw what they were about, some of them came running out of the Woods, and coming as near as they could to our Men, kneel'd down, and cry'd, *Oa*, *Oa*, *Waramokoa*, and some other Words of their Language, which none of the others understood any thing of; but as they made pitiful Gestures, and strange Noises, it was easy to understand, they begg'd to have their Boats spar'd, and that they would be gone, and never come there again.

But our Men were now satisfy'd, that they had no Way to preserve themselves, or to save their Colony, but effectually to prevent any of these People from ever going Home again; depending upon this, that if ever so much as one of them got back into their Country to tell the Story, the Colony was undone; so that letting them know that they should not have any Mercy, they fell to work with their Canoes, and destroy'd them every one, that the Storm had not destroy'd before; at the Sight of which, the Savages rais'd a hideous Cry in the Woods, which our People heard plain enough; after which, they ran about the Island like distracted Men; so that, in a Word, our Men did not really know at first what to do with them.

Nor did the *Spaniards*, with all their Prudence, consider, that while they made those People thus desperate, they ought to have kept good Guard at the same Time upon their Plantations; for tho' it is true, they had driven away their Cattle, and the *Indians* did not find out their main Retreat, I mean my old Castle at the Hill, nor the Cave in the Valley, yet they found out my Plantation at the Bower and pull'd it all to Pieces, and all the Fences and Planting about it; trod all the Corn under Foot; tore up the Vines and Grapes, being just then almost ripe, and did to our Men an inestimable Damage, tho' to themselves not one Farthing-worth of Service.

Tho' our Men were able to fight them upon all Occasions, yet they were in no Condition to pursue them, or hunt them up and down; for as they were too nimble of Foot for our Men, when they found them single, so our Men durst not go about single, for fear of being surrounded with their Numbers. The best was they had no Weapons, for tho' they had Bows they had no Arrows left, nor any Materials to make any, nor had they any edg'd Tool or Weapon among them.

The Extremity and Distress they were reduc'd to was great, and indeed deplorable; but at the same Time, our Men were also brought to very bad Circumstances by them; for tho' their Retreats were preserv'd, yet their

Provision was destroy'd, and their Harvest spoil'd, and what to do, or which Way to turn themselves, they knew not: The only Refuge they had now, was the Stock of Cattle they had in the Valley by the Cave, and some little Corn which grew there; and the Plantation of the three *Englishmen*, *William Atkins* and his Comrades, who were now reduc'd to two, one of them being kill'd by an Arrow which struck him on the Side of his Head, just under the Temple, so that he never spoke more; and it was very remarkable, that this was the same barbarous Fellow who cut the poor Savage Slave with his Hatchet, and who afterwards intended to have murder'd all the *Spaniards*.

I look'd upon their Case to have been worse at this Time, than mine was at any Time, after I first discover'd the Grains of Barley and Rice, and got into the Manner of planting and raising my Corn, and my tame Cattle; for now they had, as I may say, a hundred Wolves upon the Island, which would devour every Thing they could come at, yet could very hardly be come at themselves.

The first Thing they concluded, when they saw what their Circumstances were, was, that they would, if possible, drive them up to the farther Part of the Island, South-West, that if any more Savages came on Shore, they might not find one another. Then, that they would daily hunt and harrass them, and kill as many of them as they could come at, till they had reduc'd their Number; and if they could at last tame them, and bring them to any Thing, they would give them Corn, and teach them how to plant and live upon their daily Labour.

In order to this, they so follow'd them, and so terrify'd them with their Guns, that in a few Days, if any of them fir'd a Gun at an *Indian*, if he did not hit him, yet he would fall down for Fear; and so dreadfully frighted they were, that they kept out of Sight farther and farther, till at laſt our Men following them, and every Day almoſt killing and wounding some of them, they kept up in the Woods and hollow Places so much, that it reduc'd them to the utmoſt Misery for want of Food, and many were afterwards found dead in the Woods, without any Hurt, but meerly ſtarv'd to Death.

When our Men found this, it made their Hearts relent, and Pity mov'd them; especially the *Spaniard* Governour, who was the moſt gentlemanly generous-minded Man as ever I met with in my Life; and he propos'd, if possible, to take one of them alive, and bring him to underſtand what they meant, so far as to be able to act as Interpreter, and to go among them, and see if they might be brought to some Conditions, that might be depended upon, to save their Lives, and to do us no Spoil.

It was some while before any of them could be taken; but being weak and half ſtarv'd, one of them was at laſt surpriz'd and made a Prisoner; he was sullen at firſt, and would neither eat or drink; but finding himself kindly used, and Victuals given him, and no Violence offer'd him, he at laſt grew tractable, and came to himself.

They brought old *Friday* to him, who talk'd often with him, and told him how kind the other would be to them all; that they would not only save their Lives, but would give them a Part of the Island to live in, provided they would give Satisfaction that they would keep in their own Bounds, and not come beyond it, to injure or prejudice others, and that they should have Corn given them, to plant and make it grow for their Bread, and some Bread given them for their present Subsiſtence; and old *Friday* bad the Fellow go and talk with the reſt of his Countrymen, and see what they said to it, assuring them, that if they did not agree immediately, they should be all destroy'd.

The poor Wretches, thoroughly humbled, and reduc'd in Number to about thirty seven, clos'd with the Proposal at the first Offer, and begg'd to have some Food given them; upon which, twelve *Spaniards* and two *Englishmen* well arm'd, with three *Indian* Slaves, and old *Friday*, march'd to the Place where they were; the three *Indian* Slaves carry'd them a large Quantity of Bread; some Rice boil'd up to Cakes, and dry'd in the Sun, and three live Goats; and they were order'd to go to the Side of a Hill, where they sat down, eat the Provisions very thankfully, and were the most faithful Fellows to their Words that could be thought of; for except when they came to beg Victuals and Directions, they never came out of their Bounds; and there they liv'd when I came to the Island, and I went to see them.

They had taught them both to plant Corn, make Bread, breed tame Goats and milk them; they wanted nothing but Wives, and they soon would have been a Nation. They were confin'd to a Neck of Land, surrounded with high Rocks behind them, and lying plain towards the Sea before them, on the South-East Corner of the Island: They had Land enough, and it was very good and fruitful: they had a Piece of Land about a Mile and half broad, three or four Mile in Length.

Our Men taught them to make wooden Spades, such as I made for myself, and gave them among them twelve Hatchets, and three or four Knives; and there they liv'd the most subjected innocent Creatures that ever were heard of.

After this, the Colony enjoy'd a perfect Tranquility

with Respect to the Savages, till I came to revisit them, which was above two Years: Not, but that now and then some Canoes of Savages came on Shore for their triumphal unnatural Feasts, but as they were of several Nations, and perhaps had never heard of those that came before, or the Reason of it, they did not make any Search or Enquiry after their Countrymen; and if they had, it would have been very hard to have found them out.

Thus, I think, I have given a full Account of all that happen'd to them, to my Return, at least that was worth Notice. The *Indians* or Savages were wonderfully civiliz'd by them, and they frequently went among them, but forbid, on Pain of Death, any one of the *Indians* coming to them, because they would not have their Settlement betray'd again.

One Thing was very remarkable, *viz.* that they taught the Savages to make Wicker-work, or Baskets; but they soon outdid their Masters; for they made Abundance of most ingenious Things in Wicker-work; particularly, all Sorts of Baskets, Sieves, Bird-Cages, Cup-boards, *&c.* as also Chairs to sit on, Stools, Beds, Couches, and Abundance of other Things, being very ingenious at such Work, when they were once put in the Way of it.

My coming was a particular Relief to these People, because we furnish'd them with Knives, Scissars, Spades, Shovels, Pick-axes, and all Things of that Kind which they could want.

With the Help of these Tools they were so very handy, that they came at last to build up their Huts, or our Houses, very handsomely; raddling or working it up like Basket-work all the way round, which was a very extraordinary Piece of Ingenuity, and look'd very odd, but was an exceeding good Fence, as well against Heat, as againſt all Sorts of Vermine; and our Men were so taken with it, that they got the wild Savages to come and do the like for them; so that when I came to see the two *Englishmens* Colonies, they look'd, at a Diſtance, as if they liv'd all like Bees in a Hive; and as for *Will. Atkins*, who was now become a very induſtrious necessary and sober Fellow, he had made himself such a Tent of Basket-work as I believe was never seen; it was 120 Paces round in the Out-side, as I measur'd by my Steps; the Walls were as close work'd as a Basket in Pannels, or Squares of 32 in Number, and very ſtrong, ſtanding about seven Foot high; in the middle was another not above 22 Paces round, but built ſtronger, being Eight-square in its Form, and in the eight Corners ſtood eight very ſtrong Poſts, round the Top of which he laid ſtrong Pieces pinn'd together with wooden Pins, from which he rais'd a Piramid for the Roof of eight Rafters, very handsome, I assure you, and join'd together very well, tho' he had no Nails, and only a few Iron Spikes, which he made himself too, out of the old Iron that I had left there; and indeed this Fellow shew'd abundance of Ingenuity in several Things, which he had no Knowledge of; he made him a Forge, with a Pair of wooden Bellows to blow the Fire; he made himself Charcoal for his Work, and he form'd out of one of the Iron Crows a middling good Anvil to hammer upon; in this Manner he made many Things, but especially Hooks, Staples and Spikes, Bolts and Hinges. But to return to the House; after he had pitch'd the Roof of his innermoſt Tent, he work'd it up between the Rafters with Basket-work, so firm, and thatch'd that over again so ingeniously with Rice-ſtraw, and over that a large Leaf of a Tree, which cover'd the Top, that his House was as dry as if it had been til'd or slated. Indeed he own'd that the Savages made the Basket-work for him.

The outer Circuit was cover'd, as a Lean-to, all round this inner Apartment, and long Rafters lay from the two and thirty Angles to the top Posts of the inner House, being about twenty Foot Distant; so that there was a Space like a Walk within the outer Wicker-wall, and without the inner, near twenty Foot wide.

The inner Place he partition'd off with the same Wicker-work, but much fairer, and divided it into six Apartments, so that he had six Rooms on a Floor; and out of every one of these there was a Door, first into the Entry or Coming into the main Tent, and another Door into the Space or Walk that was round it; so that Walk was also divided into six equal Parts, which serv'd not only for Retreat, but to store up any Necessaries which the Family had Occasion for. These six Spaces not taking up the whole Circumference, what other Apartments the outer Circle had, were thus order'd: As soon as you were in at the Door of the outer Circle, you had a short Passage strait before you to the Door of the inner House, but on either Side was a wicker Partition, and a Door in it, by which you went, first, into a large Room or Store-house, twenty Foot wide, and about thirty Foot long, and thro' that into another not quite so long; so that in the outer Circle was ten handsome Rooms, six of which were only to be come at thro' the Apartments of the inner Tent, and serv'd as Closets or retiring Rooms to the respective Chambers of the inner Circle; and four large Warehouses or Barns, or what you please to call them, which went in thro' one another, two on either Hand of the Passage, that led thro' the outer Door to the inner Tent.

Such a Piece of Basket-work, I believe, was never seen in the World, nor House, or Tent, so neatly contriv'd, much less, so built. In this great Bee-hive liv'd the three Families, that is to say, *Will. Atkins* and his Companion; the third was kill'd, but his Wife remain'd with three Children; for she was, it seems, big with Child when he dy'd, and the other two were not at all backward to give the Widow her full Share of every Thing, I mean, as to their Corn, Milk, Grapes, *&c.* and when they kill'd a Kid or found a Turtle on the Shore; so that they all liv'd well enough, tho' it was true, they were not so industrious as the other two, as has been observ'd already.

One thing, however, cannot be omitted, *viz.* That as for Religion, I don't know that there was any Thing of that Kind among them; they pretty often indeed put one another in Mind that there was a God, by the very common Method of Seamen, *viz.* Swearing by his Name: Nor were their poor ignorant Savage-Wives much the better for having been marry'd to Christians, as we must call them; for as they knew very little of God themselves, so they were utterly uncapable of entering into any Discourse with their Wives about a God, or to talk any thing to them concerning Religion.

The utmost of all the Improvement which I can say the Wives had made from them, was, that they had taught them to speak *English* pretty well, and all the Children they had, which was near 20 in all, were taught to speak *English* too, from their first learning to speak, tho' they at first spoke it in a very broken Manner, like their Mothers. There were none of these Children above six Years old when I came thither, for it was not much above seven Years that they had fetch'd these five Savage Ladies over, but they had all been pretty fruitful, for they had all Children, more or less: I think the Cook's Mate's Wife was big of her sixth Child; and the Mothers were all a good Sort of well-govern'd, quiet, laborious Women, modest and decent, helpful to one another; mighty observant and subject to their Masters, I cannot call them Husbands; and wanted nothing but to be well instructed in the Christian Religion, and to be legally marry'd; both which were happily brought about afterwards by my Means, or, at least, in Consequence of my coming among them.

END OF THE SECOND VOLUME